CALIFORNIA EDITION

WORKBOOK

HARCOURT SCIENCE

Harcourt School Publishers

Orlando • Boston • Dallas • Chicago • San Diego

www.harcourtschool.com

ISBN 0-15-317678-4

2 3 4 5 6 7 8 9 10 022   2002 2001 2000

Harcourt

Contents

Harcourt

Matter and Energy

Extension

Harcourt

Reading in Science

Reading is very important in your becoming an independent learner—in being able to find, understand, and apply the information you need in the classroom and in your life. In science reading you are expected to find information, learn the meanings of scientific words, and put together ideas and observations. You can be helped in this reading and understanding by using the following suggestions.

To help you locate topics in *Harcourt Science* and most other science texts, use the:

- table of contents,
- titles of units, chapters, and lessons,
- headings and subheadings,
- index.

Look for and read these parts of a lesson in *Harcourt Science* to locate main ideas and other key information:

- Vocabulary Preview
- Investigate activity
- Process Skill Tip
- Find Out
- ✓ questions
- Picture captions
- Inside Story
- Summary
- Review
- Links
- Features

To help you recognize and read for specific kinds of information:

1. Recognize the text structure by looking for signal words
   - compare/contrast—*however, but, some, different, instead, on the other hand, like, unlike, both, neither*
   - sequence or how-to—*first, second, next, then, last, finally,* or the use of numbered steps
   - cause/effect—*since, because, as a result*

Harcourt

Name _____

2. Preview the material to see at a glance which material you already know something about and which contains new or unfamiliar topics.

3. First, read the questions at the end of a lesson or chaper, then read the lesson or chapter to find the answers. Also use the **Find Out** statements to help you identify what you need to find out while reading.

4. Construct graphic organizers or use the graphic organizers provided in the workbook to help you remember key points as you read.

5. Read the Science **Process Skill Tip** in each investigation to help you understand the meaning of a process skill. Do the Process Skill Practice page in the workbook for more information.

6. Write a summary of the main ideas of a lesson. Put in your own words (paraphrase) what you read about. Then compare your summary to the lesson summary in the book.

7. Look for comparison words such as *like* or *similar to*. These words can help you to understand something new by comparing it to something you already know about.

8. Read the entire sentence and sometimes the sentences around highlighted vocabulary to tell you what these words mean.

9. Make an outline of what you read to record main points.

10. Ask questions as you read. Write facts in one column on a sheet of paper. Write your questions in the column next to the facts.

11. Reflect on what you read. Write notes not only about what you read, but also about what you think, and why.

12. Use the **Review** in the text and the **Concept Review** and **Vocabulary Review** in the workbook to help you prepare for the chapter test.

Harcourt

Chapter 1 • Graphic Organizer for Chapter Concepts

From Single Cells to Body Systems

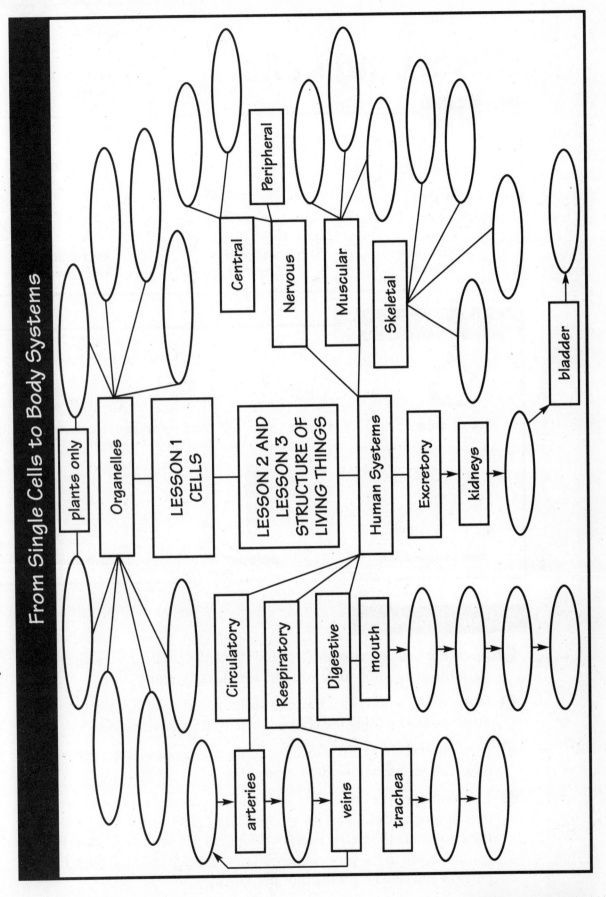

plants only

Organelles

LESSON 1
CELLS

LESSON 2 AND
LESSON 3
STRUCTURE OF
LIVING THINGS

Central

Peripheral

Nervous

Muscular

Skeletal

bladder

Human Systems

Excretory

kidneys

Circulatory

Respiratory

Digestive

mouth

arteries

veins

trachea

Name _____

Date _____

Observing Cells

Materials

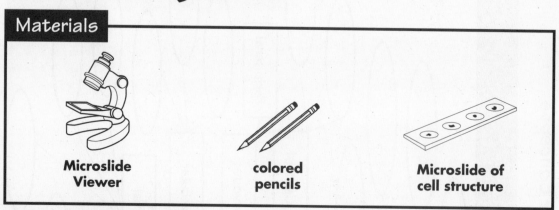

Microslide Viewer colored pencils Microslide of cell structure

Alternate Materials

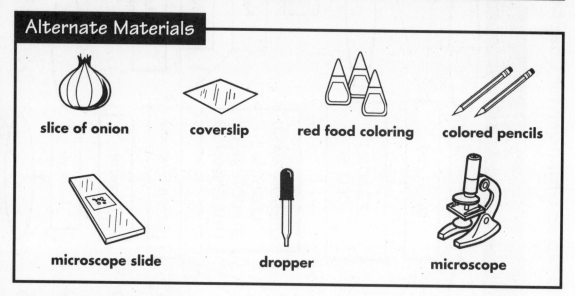

slice of onion coverslip red food coloring colored pencils

microscope slide dropper microscope

Activity Procedure

1 Insert the Cell Structure Microslide in the slot on the Microslide Viewer. Turn the focus knob until you can see the cells clearly.

2 **Observe** the onion skin cells and the human cheek cells. **Record** your observations by using the colored pencils to make drawings.

3 Now **observe** the green leaf cells and the nerve cells. Again, **record** your observations by making drawings.

4 Now **compare** your drawings. Make a Venn diagram with two large, overlapping circles. Label the circles *Plant Cells* and *Animal Cells*. Label the area where the circles overlap *Both Cells*. Draw the cell parts that you **observed** in the proper circles. Leave enough room to label the parts as you read about them in this lesson.

Harcourt

Name _____

Investigate Log

Draw Conclusions

1. **Compare** the outer layers of plant and animal cells. _____

_____

_____

2. In the centers of most cells are structures that control the cells' activities. How many of these structures are there in each of the cells you **observed**?

_____

3. **Scientists at Work** Scientists often **infer** characteristics of a group of objects by **observing** just a few of the objects. From your observations, what do you infer about the number of controlling structures in a cell? _____

_____

_____

Investigate Further Now that you have **observed** photomicrographs of cells, what questions do you have about living cells? Use the materials in the *Alternate Materials* list to **plan and conduct a simple investigation** based on your questions. Write instructions that others can follow in carrying out the investigation. See page R5 for tips on using a microscope. _____

_____

_____

_____

_____

Harcourt

Name _____

Date _____

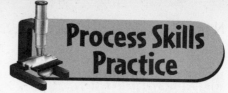

Observe and Infer

Observing is the most basic science skill. Making good observations
will allow you to develop other important science skills, like inferring,
comparing, classifying, and measuring. Inferring involves the use
of logical reasoning to make conclusions based on observations.
Inferences are explanations for events, are based on judgments,
and are not always correct.

Think About Observing and Inferring

You looked at cells during the investigation for this lesson. Imagine you come to
class and find that all the microscope slides have been removed from their holders
and had their labels removed. Use your observations and your knowledge of cells
to answer the following questions and make inferences.

1. Your teacher asks you and other students to help relabel the slides by
   separating the cell slides from the other slides. What do you need to look

   for to decide whether or not you are looking at a cell slide? _____

   _____

   _____

2. Next your teacher asks you to separate the plant cell slides from the animal cell
   slides. What do you need to look for to decide whether or not you are looking

   at a plant cell slide or an animal cell slide? _____

   _____

   _____

3. What would you look for to decide whether you were seeing that structure?

   _____

   _____

4. What inference could you make about why such a difference is found in plant

   and animal cells? _____

   _____

   _____

Harcourt

What Are Cells, and What Do They Do?

Lesson Concept

Living things are made of one or more cells, each able to support the functions of life. Plant cells differ from animal cells in that they have cell walls and chloroplasts.

Vocabulary

cell (A6)	**cell membrane** (A8)	**nucleus** (A8)
cytoplasm (A9)	**diffusion** (A10)	**osmosis** (A10)
tissue (A12)	**organ** (A12)	**system** (A12)

Match the name of each structure or process with its function.

_____ **1.** muscle tissue

_____ **2.** chromosomes

__A__ **3.** passive transport

_____ **4.** diffusion

_____ **5.** nervous tissue

_____ **6.** active transport

_____ **7.** chloroplasts

_____ **8.** cell membrane

_____ **9.** nucleus

_____ **10.** vacuoles

A energy-free movement of materials through a cell membrane

B make food in plant cells

C store food, water, and waste materials for the cell

D can move an animal's skeleton by contracting and relaxing

E holds parts of the cell together and separates the cell from its surroundings

F the way most materials move in and out of cells

G threadlike structures that contain information about the characteristics of the organism

H carries electrical signals that affect muscle tissue

I controls the cell's activities

J use of a carrier and energy from a cell to transport materials through the cell

Harcourt

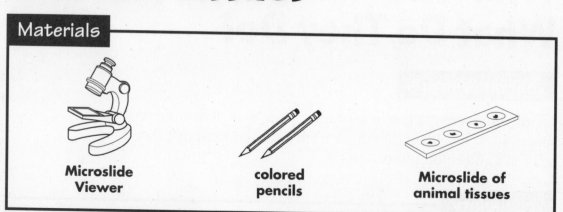
Cells and Tissues

Materials

Microslide Viewer

colored pencils

Microslide of animal tissues

Alternate Materials

prepared slides of epithelial, connective, and nervous tissues

microscope

Activity Procedure

1 Insert the Animal Tissues Microslide in the slot of the Microslide Viewer. Turn the focus knob until you can see the cells and tissues clearly.

2 **Observe** the voluntary muscle cells. **Record** your observations by using the colored pencils to make a drawing. Label your drawing with the name of the tissue. Then describe the tissue. You may use the Microslide text folder to help you write your description.

3 Repeat Step 2 for the smooth muscle cells and the heart muscle.

4 **Compare** the three kinds of muscle tissue.

Harcourt

Name _____

Draw Conclusions

1. How are the three kinds of muscle tissue alike? How are they different?

_____

_____

_____

_____

2. The dark-stained organelles you **observed** in the muscle tissues are mitochondria. Which kind of muscle tissue has the most mitochondria?

_____

3. **Scientists at Work** When scientists **compare** objects, they often **infer** reasons for any differences. What do you infer about why one kind of muscle tissue has more mitochondria than the others? _____

_____

_____

Investigate Further Now that you have **observed** several kinds of tissues, develop a testable question about differences among tissues. Use the materials in the *Alternate Materials* list to study other kinds of tissue. Observe the tissues under the microscope, and draw and label any differences you see. **Infer** how these tissues are different from the muscle tissues you observed. See page R5 for tips on using a microscope. _____

_____

_____

_____

Harcourt

Name _____

Date _____

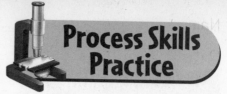

Process Skills Practice

Compare and Infer

When you compare data, you arrange your information so that you can see similarities and differences. Inferring involves the use of logical reasoning to make conclusions based on observations.

Think About Comparing and Inferring

Rajean was doing a comparative study to test a new preservative. She made a nutrient solution for microorganisms from beef broth. Then she put 100 mL of the broth in three different beakers. She put 0.1 mL of the preservative in *Beaker A*, 0.01 mL in *Beaker B*, and 0.001 mL in *Beaker C*. The next day Rajean checked the beakers and found the broth discolored and cloudy in two of them. So, she used a microscope to check a sample from each of the three beakers. She recorded what she observed.

	Beaker A	Beaker B	Beaker C
Amount of preservative added to beaker	0.1 mL	0.01 mL	0.001 mL
Appearance of broth	Clear	Somewhat cloudy	Very cloudy
Microorganisms seen under microscope	None	Yeast cells	Yeast and bacteria

1. Compare the mixtures in each beaker. How are they different?

   _____

2. How are they alike? _____

   _____

3. After 24 hours, how do the beakers compare? _____

   _____

4. What can you infer about how effective the preservative is in keeping yeast

   from growing in the solution? _____

   _____

Harcourt

How Do Body Systems Transport Materials?

Lesson Concept

Body cells are organized into tissues, organs, and systems that work together to keep the body alive. Four of the major systems are the circulatory, the respiratory, the digestive, and the excretory.

Vocabulary

capillaries (A17)   **alveoli** (A18)   **villi** (A19)   **nephrons** (A20)

Match the name of each structure or process with its function.

_____ **1.** circulatory system

_____ **2.** platelets

_____ **3.** alveoli

_____ **4.** esophagus

_____ **5.** capillaries

_____ **6.** ureters

_____ **7.** trachea

_____ **8.** arteries

_____ **9.** heart

_____ **10.** saliva

_____ **11.** pancreas

_____ **12.** sweating

A blood vessels so small that blood cells have to move through them in single file

B a long tube that leads to the stomach

C transports oxygen, nutrients, and wastes through the body in the blood

D tubes that empty wastes into the bladder from the kidneys

E vessels through which blood leaves the heart

F moistens food and begins to break down starchy foods

G pumps blood through blood vessels

H cause blood to clot when a blood vessel is cut

I eliminates excess body heat

J sometimes called the windpipe

K tiny air sacs in the lungs

L produces a fluid that neutralizes stomach acid

Harcourt

Use with page A21.

Name _____

Date _____

How Muscles Cause Movement

Materials

tape measure

Activity Procedure

1 Place your left hand on top of your right arm, between the shoulder and elbow. Bend and straighten your right arm at the elbow. **Observe** the movement by feeling the muscles in your right arm.

2 The muscle on the front of the upper arm is called the *biceps*. The muscle on the back of the upper arm is called the *triceps*. **Compare** the biceps and the triceps as you bend and straighten your arm. **Infer** which muscle controls the bending movement and which controls the straightening movement.

3 Have a partner use the tape measure to **measure** the distance around your upper arm when it is straight and when it is bent. **Record** the measurements.

4 Repeat Steps 2 and 3, using your right hand and your left arm.

5 **Compare** the sets of measurements.

Harcourt

Name _____

Draw Conclusions

1. What did you **infer** about the muscles controlling the bending and the straightening of your upper arm? _____

_____

_____

2. Why are two muscles needed to bend and straighten your arm? Why can't one muscle do it? _____ _____

_____

_____

3. **Scientists at Work** Scientists often **hypothesize** about things they **observe**. Hypothesize about any differences between the measurements of your right arm and the measurements of your left arm. _____

_____

_____

Investigate Further Repeat the investigation with different pairs of muscles. For example, try bending your leg at the knee while **observing** the muscles in your thigh. See if these measurements also support your hypothesis. Draw conclusions about differences in muscle sizes from the data you collected. Decide whether more data is needed to support your conclusions. _____

_____

_____

_____

Harcourt

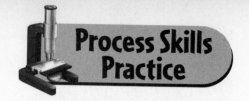

Hypothesize

When you hypothesize, you make an educated guess about the results of an experiment you plan to do. A hypothesis is based upon observation, prior knowledge, and prior experimental outcomes. A hypothesis is often altered based on the outcome of experiments that test it.

Think About Hypothesizing

A group of students decided to test the effect of sleep and repeated trials on reaction time. Their hypothesis was that reaction time would improve with more sleep and repeated trials. Each student in the test was asked to push a button as soon as he or she heard the sound of a bell. The amount of time between the sound of the bell and the pushing of the button was recorded as the reaction time.

The table below lists reaction times for three students on different days after receiving different amounts of sleep the night before. Each student underwent two trials on each day of testing.

| Amount of Sleep | Reaction Time in Seconds | | | | | |
| | Student A | | Student B | | Student C | |
	Trial 1	Trial 2	Trial 1	Trial 2	Trial 1	Trial 2
8 hours	0.20	0.16	0.15	0.12	0.25	0.19
6 hours	0.17	0.17	0.19	0.24	0.25	0.32
4 hours	0.30	0.45	0.35	0.47	0.40	0.45
2 hours	0.82	1.10	0.75	1.08	0.80	1.02

1. Was the hypothesis correct? _____

2. Use the data to form a hypothesis about the effect of sleeping less than eight hours a night on reaction time. _____

   _____

   _____

3. How would you test this hypothesis? _____

   _____

Harcourt

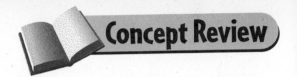

How Do Bones, Muscles, and Nerves Work Together?

Lesson Concept

Skeletal bones move because of the action of pairs of voluntary muscles. Smooth muscles line digestive organs and blood vessels. The walls of the heart are made of cardiac muscle. Nerves carry signals from sensory organs to the brain and from the brain to the muscles.

Vocabulary

bone marrow (A24)	**joints** (A24)	**tendons** (A25)
ligaments (A25)	**neuron** (A26)	**receptors** (A26)

Match the term in the left column with its description in the right column.

_____ 1. bone marrow

_____ 2. ligaments

_____ 3. tendons

_____ 4. smooth muscles

_____ 5. cardiac muscles

_____ 6. joints

_____ 7. central nervous system

_____ 8. receptors

_____ 9. neurons

_____ 10. dendrites

_____ 11. axon

_____ 12. synapse

A line digestive organs and blood vessels

B is made up of the brain and the spinal cord

C is the part of the neuron that carries signals and transmits them to other neurons

D are nerve cells that detect conditions in the body's environment

E attach bones to muscles

F branch out of the nerve cell and receive signals from other cells

G produces red and white blood cells

H make up the walls of the heart

I is a gap between the axon of one neuron and the dendrite of the next neuron

J attach bones to each other

K are the cells that nerves are made of

L are where the bones meet to attach to each other and to muscles

Harcourt

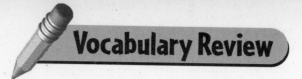

Recognize Vocabulary

Listed below are scrambled vocabulary terms from Chapter 1. Use the clues to unscramble the terms. Write the unscrambled terms on the lines provided.

1. S M O O S S I _____
the movement of water and dissolved materials through cell membranes

2. L L R C A S E I A P I _____
blood vessels so small that blood cells move through them in single file

3. R U N N E O _____
a specialized cell that can receive and transmit signals to other cells like it

4. L Y M O C P S T A _____
a jellylike substance containing chemicals that keep the cell functioning

5. G R O A N _____
tissues that work together form this

6. L C L E _____
the basic unit of structure and function of all living things

7. J S T O N I _____
where bones meet and are attached to each other and to muscles

8. P R E E T O C R S _____
nerve cells that detect conditions in the body's environment

9. I I L V L _____
tiny tubes sticking out from the walls of the small intestine

10. O M N O E A W B R R (2 words) _____
connective tissue that produces red and white blood cells

11. F D N I U F I O S _____
the way most materials move in and out of cells

12. M C L N E E M E R L B A (2 words) _____
a thin covering that encloses a cell

13. I G L E S A N T M _____
bands of connective tissue that hold the skeleton together

14. V I O A L E L _____
tiny air sacs at the end of the smallest tubes in the lungs

Harcourt

Chapter 2 • Graphic Organizer for Chapter Concepts

Classifying Living Things

LESSON 1
CLASSIFYING

Why Classify?

_____

_____

The Five Kingdoms

1. _____

2. _____

3. _____

4. _____

5. _____

LESSON 2
CLASSIFYING ANIMALS

Animals with Backbones Are

Called _____ .

Examples

1. _____

2. _____

3. _____

4. _____

5. _____

Animals Without Backbones

Are Called _____ .

LESSON 3
CLASSIFYING PLANTS

Two Groups of Plants

1. _____

2. _____

Name _____

Date _____

Classifying Shoes

Materials

shoes

newspaper or
paper towels

Activity Procedure

1 Take off one shoe and put it with your classmates' shoes. If you put the shoes on a desk or table, cover it first with newspaper or paper towels.

2 Find a way to **classify** the shoes. Begin by finding two or three large groups of shoes that are alike. Write a description of each group.

3 **Classify** the large groups of shoes into smaller and smaller groups. Each smaller group should be alike in some way.

My classification: _____

_____

_____

4 Write a description of each smaller group.

My descriptions: _____

_____

_____

_____

_____

5 Stop classifying when you have sorted all the shoes into groups with two or fewer members.

Harcourt

Name _____

Draw Conclusions

1. What features did you use to **classify** the shoes? _____

_____

_____

2. **Compare** your classification system with a classmate's system. How are your

systems alike? _____

_____

_____

How are they different? _____

_____

_____

3. **Scientists at Work** Scientists **classify** living things to show how living things
are alike. Why might it be important for scientists to agree on a set of rules for

classifying living things? _____

_____

_____

_____

_____

Investigate Further Classify other groups of things such as toys, cars, or pictures
of plants and animals. Write a brief explanation of your classification system.

_____

_____

_____

Harcourt

Name _____

Date _____

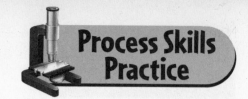

Classify

When you classify living things, you group them based on similarities.
Things with many similarities may be classified in more than one way.

Think About Classifying

Observe these pictures of shells. Classify the
shells into two or more groups. Fill in the
chart to describe your classification
system. Then answer the questions.

Characteristic Used for Classifying	Name of Group	Shells in Group

1. Look at the shells in each of your groups. How could you classify the shells in
   each group into smaller groups? _____

   _____

   _____

   _____

2. Compare your classification with that of a classmate. How were your
   classifications similar? How were they different? _____

   _____

   _____

Harcourt

How Do Scientists Classify Living Things?

Lesson Concept

Scientists organize living things so they can be easily studied and discussed.

Vocabulary

classification (A38)   **kingdom** (A39)   **moneran** (A39)   **protist** (A39)

fungi (A39)   **genus** (A40)   **species** (A40)

Answer the questions below.

1. Fill in the missing information on the chart about living things.

The Kingdoms		
Kingdom	**Important Characteristics**	**Examples**
		Monkeys, birds, frogs, fish, and spiders
Plants		Trees, flowers, ferns, and mosses
	Most many-celled, absorb food from other living things	
Protists		Algae, amoebas, and diatoms
	One-celled, no cell nuclei; some make their own food, some feed on living things	

2. The white oak tree has the scientific name *Quercus alba*. This is also the name

of the _____. What genus does the white oak belong

to? _____ What kingdom does the white oak tree

belong to? _____

Harcourt

Building a Model Backbone

Materials

chenille stem

wagon wheel pasta, uncooked

candy gelatin rings

Activity Procedure

1 Bend one end of the chenille stem. Thread six pieces of wagon-wheel pasta onto the stem. Push the pasta down to the bend in the stem. Bend the stem above the pasta to hold the pasta in place.

2 Bend and twist the stem. What do you see and hear? _____

_____

3 Take all the pasta off the chenille stem except one. Thread a candy gelatin ring onto the stem, and push it down.

4 Add pasta and rings until the stem is almost full. Bend the stem above the pasta and rings to hold them in place.

5 Bend and twist the stem. What do you see and hear? _____

_____

6 Draw pictures of the model backbones you made. **Compare** your models with that shown in the picture on page A57.

Harcourt

Name _____

Draw Conclusions

1. A real backbone is made of bones called vertebrae (VER•tuh•bree) and soft discs that surround the spinal cord. What does each part of your final model stand

   for? _____

   _____

   _____

   _____

2. How is your final model like a real backbone? _____

   _____

   _____

   _____

3. Study your final model again. What do the soft discs do? _____

   _____

   _____

   _____

4. **Scientists at Work** Scientists **use models** to study how things work. Would a piece of dry, uncooked spaghetti or some other material work better than a chenille stem to stand for the spinal cord in your model? Try it and see. Then write a report of your investigation. Be sure to include the results of any tests you conducted with other materials, and any conclusions you drew about

   using those materials in your model backbone. _____

   _____

   _____

   _____

   _____

Harcourt

Name _____

Date _____

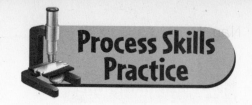

Make a Model

You don't always need to see the whole thing to understand how part of it works. Models can be built to help you see just one part of a thing.

Think About Making a Model

Todd wanted to show his younger sister Rebecca how a frog leaps. He decided to make a poster to show the leaping movements of a frog. He found a book with pictures of a frog leaping. The book showed that when a frog leaps, it makes six basic movements.

  First the frog crouches down, bending all its legs. Then its feet and legs move straight out away from its body, pushing the frog away from the crouched position. While in midair, it pulls its front legs back to its sides and leaves its hind legs straight. Right before the frog lands, it puts its front legs in front of itself. The frog lands on its front feet first. Then it pulls its back legs toward its body and puts them on the ground.

1. Why would it be hard to understand the movements by just watching a

   frog leap? _____

   _____

2. Why do you think Todd made a poster instead of a working model of a frog?

   _____

   _____

3. Do you think Todd's poster was a model? Explain. _____

   _____

   _____

   _____

4. Besides Todd's poster, what other ways could Rebecca use to learn about how

   a frog leaps? _____

   _____

Harcourt

How Are Vertebrates Classified?

Lesson Concept

Animals with backbones are classified into five groups.

Vocabulary

vertebrate (A44)   **mammal** (A44)   **reptile** (A44)   **amphibian** (A44)

invertebrate (A45)   **bird** (A45)   **fish** (A45)

Fill in the missing information on the chart.

Group	Important Characteristics	Examples
	Have moist skin and scales; begin life in water	Frogs,
	Have wings and feathers; lay eggs	Eagles, owls,
	Have scales; spend their entire lives in water	Salmon, trout, and
Mammals		Cats, dogs, and
Reptiles		Lizards, snakes,

Plant Stems

Materials

fresh celery stalk with leaves

plastic knife

two containers

water

red food coloring

blue food coloring

hand lens

paper towels

Activity Procedure

1 Use the plastic knife to trim the end off the celery stalk. Split the celery from the middle of the stalk to the bottom. Do not cut the stalk completely in half.

2 Use the chart below.

3 Half-fill each container with water. Add 15 drops of red food coloring to one container. Add 15 drops of blue food coloring to the other container.

4 With the containers side by side, place one part of the celery stalk in each container of colored water. You may need to prop the stalk up so the containers don't tip over.

5 **Observe** the celery every 15 minutes for an hour. **Record** your observations on your chart.

6 After you have completed your chart, put a paper towel on your desk. Take the celery out of the water. Cut about 2 cm off the bottom of the stalk. Use the hand lens to **observe** the pieces of stalk and freshly cut end of the stalk.

Time	Observations

Harcourt

Name _____

Draw Conclusions

1. Where did the water travel? _____

_____

How do you know? _____

_____

2. How fast did the water travel? _____

_____

How do you know? _____

_____

3. Scientists at Work Scientists **infer** what happens in nature by making careful observations. Based on this investigation, what can you infer about the

importance of stems? _____

_____

_____

Investigate Further How could you change a white carnation into a flower with two colors? Draw and write an explanation of your answer.

_____

My Explanation: _____

_____

_____

Harcourt

Name _____

Date _____

Infer

Inferring is using what you observe to explain what has happened. An inference may be correct or incorrect. Once you have made an inference, you may need to make more observations to confirm your inference.

Think About Inferring

Hope was helping decorate her house with flowers she cut from her garden. She made two similar bouquets in different vases with water. The pictures show what happened to Hope's bouquets after a few days. After the third day, Hope wondered why the flowers in the black vase stayed fresh, but those in the smaller white vase wilted. She looked inside the black vase. There was water in it. She looked inside the white vase. It was completely dry.

Day 1

Day 2

Day 3

1. What observations did Hope make? _____

_____

_____

2. Infer why the flowers in the white vase wilted, but those in the black vase did

   not. _____

_____

_____

3. What do you infer happened to the water in the white vase?

_____

_____

4. How could you test your inference? _____

_____

Harcourt

Use with page A49.

How Are Plants Classified?

Lesson Concept

Plants are classified by whether or not they have tubes.

Vocabulary

vascular plant (A50)   **nonvascular plant** (A52)

Fill in the blank with the letter of the correct answer.

1. The main difference between plants and animals is that _____.
   A animals make their own food   **B** plants make their own food

2. In plants with tubes, the tubes _____.
   A take in air from around the plant
   B carry water, food, and nutrients to different plant parts

3. Where would you look for tubes in a plant? _____
   A in the stem   **B** in the leaves   **C** in the trunk   **D** all of these

4. In plants that do not have tubes, food travels in water _____.
   A around the outside of the plant   **B** from cell to cell

5. Nonvascular plants are always _____.
   A very small   **B** found in dry places

6. The _____ is the part of a tree trunk that has the living tubes.
   A heartwood   **B** sapwood

7. This tree was _____ when the trunk was cut down.
   A eight years old   **B** ten years old

8. Label the parts
   of the tree trunk.

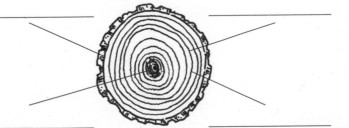

Recognize Vocabulary

Match the definition in column A with the term in column B.

Column A

_____	**1.** name of the second smallest group
_____	**2.** animal with a backbone
_____	**3.** plants with tubes
_____	**4.** grouping things by a set of rules
_____	**5.** name of the largest group
_____	**6.** have many cells and absorb food from other living things
_____	**7.** name of the smallest group
_____	**8.** invertebrates with legs and several joints
_____	**9.** plants without tubes
_____	**10.** some one-celled with no nuclei
_____	**11.** vertebrate that has fur and makes milk
_____	**12.** invertebrates that may or may not have a hard shell
_____	**13.** animal without a backbone
_____	**14.** vertebrate that begins life in water
_____	**15.** one-celled, no nuclei
_____	**16.** vertebrate with dry, scaly skin

Column B

A mollusks

B fungi

C amphibian

D classification

E invertebrate

F nonvascular plants

G genus

H reptile

I kingdom

J mammal

K monerans

L species

M vascular plants

N protists

O arthropods

P vertebrate

Use with pages A36–A53.

Harcourt

Name _____ Date _____

Plants and Their Adaptations

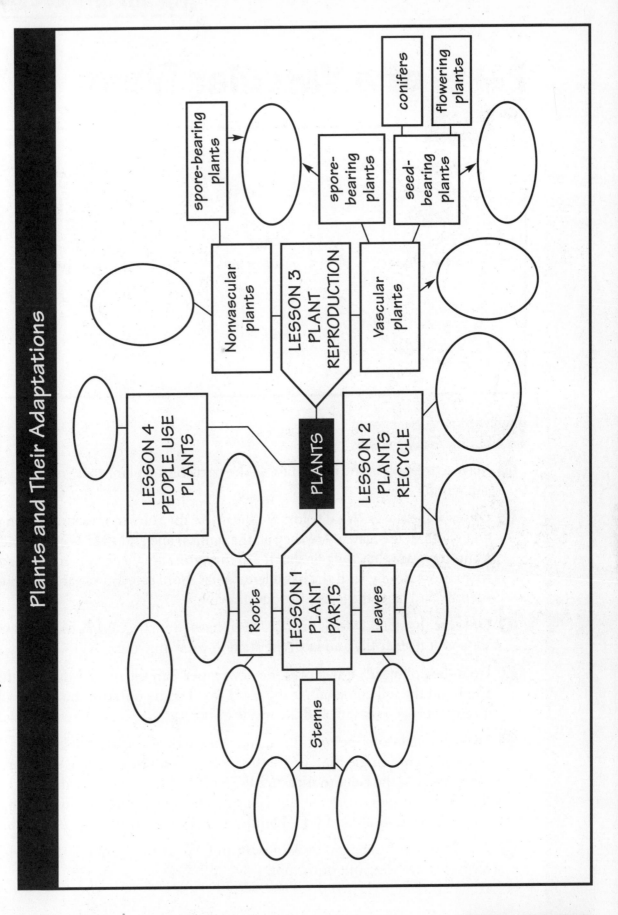

Parts of a Vascular Plant

Materials

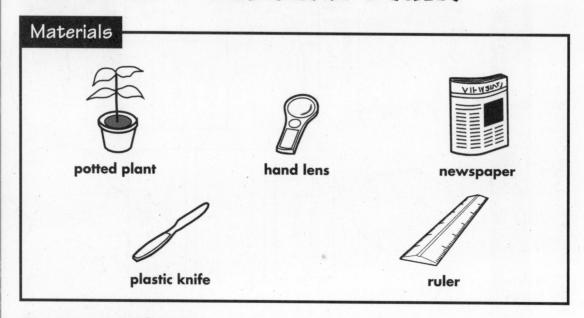

potted plant

hand lens

newspaper

plastic knife

ruler

Activity Procedure

1. Make a drawing of the plant. List all the parts of the plant that you can name.

2. **Observe** the leaves. What colors are they? Use the ruler to measure the length and width of the leaves. Are they all the same shape and size? Are they wide or narrow? Are they long or short? Do they grow singly or in pairs? Observe them more closely with the hand lens. What more can you say about them? Identify and label the leaves in your drawing.

3. **Observe** the stem. Does it bend? Does it have branches? What more can you say about it? Identify and label the stem in your drawing.

4. Hold the pot upside down over the newspaper. Tap the pot gently until the plant and the soil come out. If the plant won't come out, run the plastic knife around between the soil and the inside of the pot.

5. Shake the soil from the roots until you can see them clearly. **Observe** the roots. Is there a single root, or are there many small roots? What shape are the roots? Use the ruler to **measure** the length of the roots. Are they thick or thin? Long or short? Use the hand lens to observe them more closely. What more can you say about them? Identify and label the roots in your drawing.

6. Put the soil and the plant back into the pot. Water the plant lightly to help it recover from being out of the pot.

Harcourt

Name _____

Draw Conclusions

1. What are the parts of the plant you **observed**? _____

_____

2. **Compare** the plant parts you identified with the parts of a large tree. How are they the same? How are they different? _____

_____

_____

_____

_____

3. **Scientists at Work** Scientists learn by making observations. What did you **observe** about each part of the plant? _____

_____

_____

_____

Investigate Further What questions about plant parts could you answer if you had other measuring tools? Develop a testable question about plant parts. Then select the appropriate tools and make the observations you need to answer your question. _____

_____

_____

_____

Harcourt

Name _____

Date _____

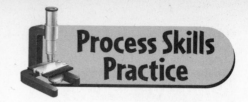

Observe

Observing involves using one or more of the senses to perceive properties of objects or events. Sometimes you need to use an instrument, such as a microscope, to extend your senses.

Think About Observing

Suppose you are walking beside a river on a summer afternoon. You observe several large slabs of concrete on the riverbank. When you look across the river, you observe more concrete slabs on the opposite bank. You are curious about them, but you decide to move on. After a short while, you come to a pipe that empties into the river. The water is foamy and cloudy near the pipe. It has no smell. You observe a lot of plants growing in the cloudy water and on the riverbank near the pipe.

1. What objects have you observed on your walk? _____

   _____

2. What senses have you used? _____

3. You observed something coming from the pipe. From your observations, do you think it was harmful to the plants? _____

   _____

   _____

4. How could you make a better observation about what was coming from the pipe? _____

5. If you decided to observe the foam more closely, what do you think you should be looking for? _____

   _____

6. If you decided to observe the concrete slabs more closely, would you need instruments to extend your senses? _____

   _____

Harcourt

Use with page A63.

Name _____

Date _____

What Are the Functions of Roots, Stems, and Leaves?

Lesson Concept

Each part of a plant has a different function. Roots anchor the plant and take in minerals and water. A stem supports the plant and moves materials between its parts. Leaves make food.

Vocabulary

xylem (A67)   **phloem** (A67)   **chlorophyll** (A68)

Match each term on the left with its description on the right.

Column A

_____ 1. fibrous roots

_____ 2. phloem

_____ 3. stomata

_____ 4. chlorophyll

_____ 5. xylem

_____ 6. taproot

_____ 7. stem

_____ 8. leaf

_____ 9. root hairs

_____ 10. chloroplasts

_____ 11. prop roots

Column B

A tiny holes in a leaf where carbon dioxide enters and oxygen exits

B a pigment that helps plants use light energy to make sugars

C a plant part that holds the plant up and carries food and water to other plant parts

D tiny parts of roots that take in water and minerals from the soil

E a root that goes straight down so it can reach water deep underground

F a plant part that is the "food factory" of the plant

G roots that form a thick and tangled mat just under the surface of the soil

H the parts of leaf cells where the food-making process takes place

I tubes in plant stems that carry water and minerals

J tubes in plant stems that carry food made in the leaves to other parts of the plant

K roots that begin above ground and keep trees that grow in loose, wet soil from being blown over by the wind

Harcourt

Use with page A69.

How Plants Use Carbon Dioxide

Materials

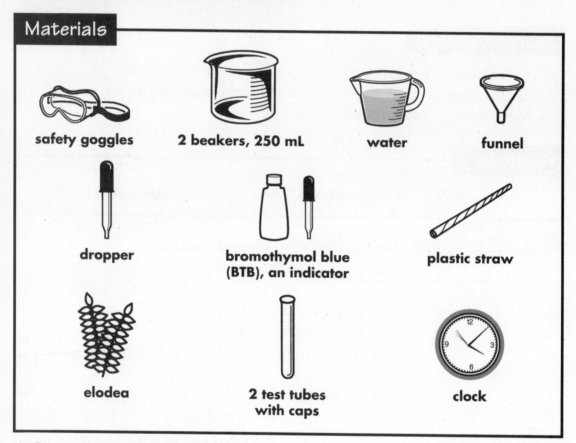

safety goggles

2 beakers, 250 mL

water

funnel

dropper

bromothymol blue (BTB), an indicator

plastic straw

elodea

2 test tubes with caps

clock

CAUTION Activity Procedure

1 **CAUTION** Put on safety goggles, and leave them on until you complete **Step 4.** Fill one beaker about two-thirds full of water. Use the dropper to add BTB to the water until you have a blue solution. BTB is an indicator. It changes color when carbon dioxide is present.

2 **CAUTION** Don't suck on the straw. If you do accidentally, don't swallow the solution. Spit it out, and rinse your mouth with water. Put the plastic straw in the solution and blow into it. What do you **observe**? **Record** your observations.

My observations: _____

3 Put the elodea into one test tube, and use the funnel to fill the tube with BTB solution from the beaker. Fill the other test tube with BTB solution only.

Harcourt

4 Seal the test tubes with caps. Carefully turn the test tubes upside down, and place them in the empty beaker.

5 Put the beaker containing the two test tubes in a sunny window for 1 hour. **Predict** what changes will occur in the test tubes. After 1 hour, **observe** both test tubes and **record** your observations.

My prediction: _____

_____

My observations: _____

_____

Draw Conclusions

1. What changes did you **observe** in the BTB solution when you blew into it

   through the straw? Explain. _____

   _____

2. What changes did you **observe** in the test tube of BTB after the elodea plant

   had been in it for 1 hour? _____

3. **Compare** the color of the BTB solution in the test tube that had the elodea
   with the color of the BTB in the test tube that did not have the elodea. Describe

   any differences. _____

   _____

4. **Scientists at Work** Scientists **observe** changes that happen during
   experiments. Then they **infer** what caused the changes. What can you infer

   about any changes that took place in the test tubes? _____

   _____

   _____

Investigate Further In this investigation the color of the BTB solution is the
dependent variable. What is the single independent variable? What did you learn
about plants using carbon dioxide from the data you collected on this variable?
Find out what would happen to the BTB solution if you changed the independent

variable. _____

_____

_____

_____

Harcourt

Name _____

Date _____

Observe and Infer

Observing is a basic science skill. Making good observations will allow you to develop other important science skills, like inferring, comparing, classifying, and measuring.

Think About Observing and Inferring

Cecelia likes to grow tomatoes. She wanted to see if adding certain things to the soil would improve her tomato harvest. She treated different parts of her garden with kitchen-scrap compost, leaf-litter compost, and nitrogen fertilizer. Some parts of the garden were not treated. For five years she treated the soil and recorded the number of tomatoes produced by the plants in each area of her garden.

	Untreated Soil	Kitchen-Scrap Compost	Leaf-Litter Compost	Nitrogen Fertilizer
Year 1	130	145	140	165
Year 2	125	155	155	155
Year 3	110	160	165	155
Year 4	95	155	170	145
Year 5	70	165	180	150

1. Which treatment produced the best results over time? _____

2. Cecelia thought she should make a bar graph of her results. Do you think it would be easier to read her data that way? _____

_____

3. What inference could you make about how Cecelia could improve the yield of plants grown in the untreated area of her garden? _____

_____

Harcourt

Name _____

Date _____

How Do Plants Recycle Materials?

Lesson Concept

Many of the materials organisms need are cycled through nature.

Vocabulary

nitrogen cycle (A73)   carbon dioxide–oxygen cycle (A74)

Choose the correct caption from the table below each diagram, and write the appropriate letter below each picture.

_____   _____   _____

A	Animal wastes and decaying organisms return nitrates and ammonia to the soil.
B	Animals get nitrogen by eating plants and other animals.
C	Plants make proteins from nitrogen in the soil.

_____   _____   _____

A	Plants use carbon dioxide and release oxygen during photosynthesis.
B	Plants and animals use oxygen and release carbon dioxide during respiration.
C	Bacteria and fungi use as food some carbon from the tissues of dead animals. The rest is released as carbon dioxide.

Harcourt

Use with page A77.

Name _____

Date _____

Nonvascular Plants

Materials

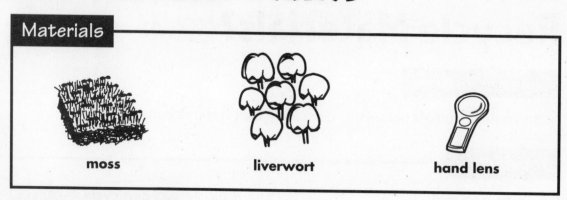

moss   liverwort   hand lens

Activity Procedure

1. **Observe** the moss and the liverwort. **Record** what you see.

2. Now **observe** the plants with a hand lens. Can you see different parts? Do any of the parts you see look like the parts of the potted plant you observed in Lesson 1?

3. **Observe** the plants by touching them with your fingers. Are they soft or firm? Are they dry or moist? What else can you tell by feeling them? Describe what they feel like.

4. Touch the plants with a pencil or other object while you **observe** them through the hand lens. Do the parts bend, or are they stiff? Do you see anything new if you push a part of the plant to one side? Describe what you see.

5. **Observe** the plants by smelling them. Do they have any kind of odor? Try to identify the odors. Describe what you smell.

6. Make drawings of the moss and liverwort, identify the parts you observed, and **infer** what each part does.

Harcourt

Name _____

Draw Conclusions

1. What plant parts did you **observe** on the moss? What parts did you observe on
   the liverwort? _____

   _____

2. What do you **infer** each part of the plant does? _____

   _____

   _____

3. **Scientists at Work** Scientists use observations to **compare** things. Use the
   observations you made in this investigation to compare the moss and

   liverwort with the plant you observed in Lesson 1. _____

   _____

   _____

Investigate Further Observe a fern. Based on your observations, would you
classify a fern as a nonvascular plant, like the moss and the liverwort, or as a vascular

plant, like the potted plant in Lesson 1? _____

_____

_____

_____

Harcourt

Name _____

Date _____

Compare

When you compare, you observe objects or events and try to find out how they are alike or different. You ask yourself questions while you are observing. Which plant is the smallest? Which plant has the most leaves? What does this plant have that the other does not have?

Think About Comparing

When you shop for fruits and vegetables, you see all different shapes and colors. You know from your experience that each of the items also has its own special taste and smell. All the shapes, the colors, the tastes, and the smells come from plants. Answer the questions about the following items: watermelon, cantaloupe, strawberries, carrots, apples, mushrooms, and lettuce.

1. Compare the mushrooms to the strawberries. Do they share any characteristics? How are they different? _____

_____

_____

_____

2. How is the carrot different from all the other items? _____

3. Compare the lettuce to all the other items. Can you think of an important difference? _____

_____

_____

_____

4. Choose the two items you think are most similar to one another. Explain your choice. _____

_____

5. Choose the two items you think are most different from one another. Explain your choice. _____

_____

Harcourt

Name _____

Date _____

How Do Plants Reproduce?

Lesson Concept

Vascular plants have xylem and phloem. Nonvascular plants do not have these tubes. Nonvascular plants and simple vascular plants reproduce with spores. Gymnosperms and angiosperms are seed-producing vascular plants. Plants go through several stages in their life cycles.

Vocabulary

spore (A81)   **gymnosperm** (A82)   **pollen** (A82)

angiosperm (A83)

Put each term on the following list into the Venn diagram below. Remember, in a Venn diagram, the areas that overlap are areas that include both categories shown in the areas. If a term belongs in or applies to both categories, put it in the area where the ovals overlap. If it belongs in or applies to only one category, put it only in the correct oval.

spore	conifer	pollen	flower
fruit	mosses	ferns	apples
xylem	phloem	chloroplasts	life cycle

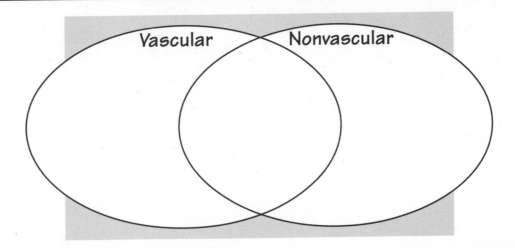

Harcourt

Name _____

Date _____

Popcorn

Materials

large plastic measuring cup

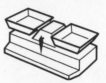
balance

unpopped popcorn

Activity Procedure

1. Cover the bottom of the measuring cup with unpopped popcorn seeds.

2. **Estimate** the volume of the unpopped seeds. Put the cup on the balance, and **measure** the mass of the unpopped seeds.

3. **Predict** what will happen to the mass and the volume when the seeds are popped.

4. Your teacher will help you pop the popcorn. Return the popped seeds to the measuring cup.

5. **Measure** the volume and mass of the cup of popped popcorn. Were your **predictions** correct?

Harcourt

Name _____

Draw Conclusions

1. How did the volume of the popcorn change? _____

_____

2. How did the mass change? Explain. _____

_____

_____

3. Scientists at Work One reason why scientists **experiment** is to test
predictions. If an experiment doesn't turn out the way they predicted, it may
mean that their predictions were wrong. Or it may mean that they did not
consider everything that could affect the experiment. Did you predict the
volume and mass of the popped popcorn correctly? Explain.

_____

_____

_____

Investigate Further What other questions do you have about popcorn? **Plan and
conduct a simple investigation** to answer your question. Write instructions that

others can follow in carrying out the procedure. _____

_____

_____

_____

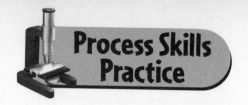

Experiment

When you experiment, you gather data to test a hypothesis. A well-designed experiment will allow you to test for certain variables while controlling others so you will know which factors affect the outcome.

Think About Experimenting

Juan and Ahmal were planning an experiment to see which of four different fertilizers would grow the biggest and healthiest plants. Juan gathered four pots from the garage, labeled them *Pot A* through *Pot D*, and filled them with dirt from his backyard. He put various seeds into each pot. He labeled the fertilizers *A* through *D* and put a teaspoon of *Fertilizer A* into *Pot A*, *Fertilizer B* in *Pot B*, and so on until each pot had a spoonful of different fertilizer. Ahmal watched him do this. Then he reminded Juan that he had not controlled his experiment. Juan agreed. They started over again.

1. What are some variables Juan should control? _____

_____

_____

2. Juan and Ahmal also need a control sample. How do they make one?

_____

_____

3. As he was filling the pots with potting soil he had bought at the hardware store, Juan thought of another problem. What if, without meaning to, they paid more attention to one of the plants, because they had already formed a hypothesis that *Fertilizer A* worked better than the others? How could they

avoid this? _____

_____

_____

4. What do you think would be the best way to gather data from this experiment?

_____

_____

Harcourt

Concept Review

How Do People Use Plants?

Lesson Concept

People eat the leaves, the stems, the roots, the seeds, the fruits, and the flowers of various plants. When they are sick, people often use medicines made from plants. In fact, many things people use every day come from plants.

Vocabulary

grain (A88)	**fiber** (A90)

Read the statements below. Put a *T* in front of the true statements and an *F* in front of the false statements. If the statement is false, write a correction in the space provided after it.

_____ **1.** People use plants more for food than for any other purpose.

_____

_____

_____ **2.** Fruits form the largest part of the Food Guide Pyramid.

_____

_____

_____ **3.** Quinine, which is made from the bark of a tree, is used to treat

measles. _____

_____

_____ **4.** Grains are the seeds of certain types of grasses. _____

_____

_____ **5.** Digitalis, which is made from the leaves of the maple tree, is a heart

medicine. _____

_____

_____ **6.** A fiber is any material that can be separated into thread.

_____

_____

Harcourt

Recognize Vocabulary

Read the clues to decide which vocabulary term to use to fill in the word puzzle.

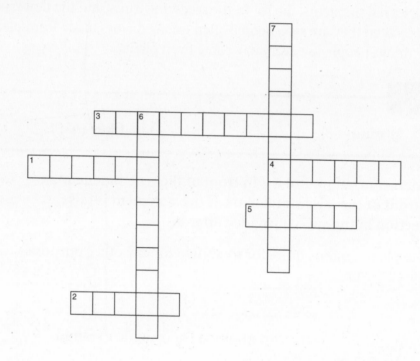

Across

1. tubes that carry food in plants

2. a reproductive cell that grows into a new plant

3. a plant with seeds covered by fruit

4. plant structures that contain male reproductive cells

5. tubes that carry water and minerals in plants

Down

6. a plant whose seeds are not protected by fruit

7. a pigment that helps plants produce sugar from light energy

Harcourt

Chapter 4 • Graphic Organizer for Chapter Concepts

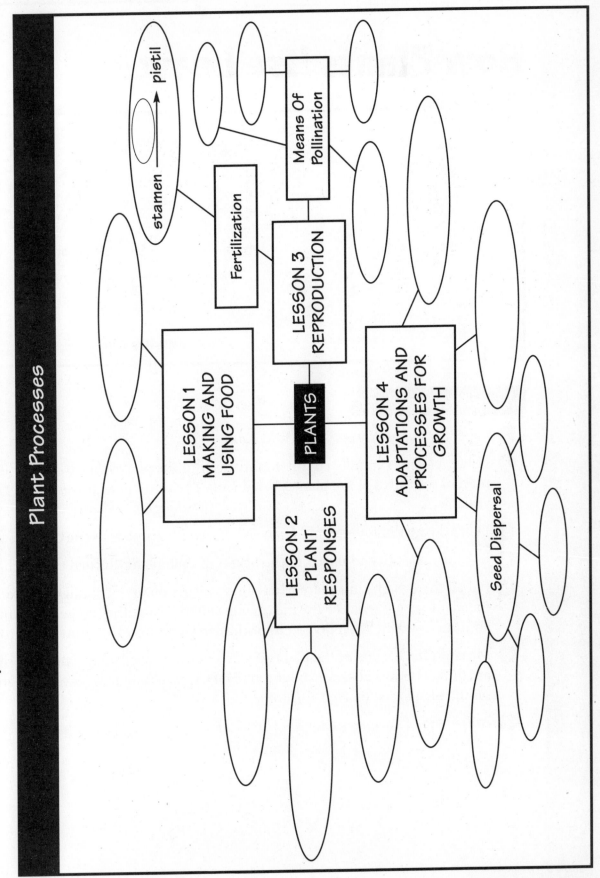

Plant Processes

stamen → pistil

Means Of Pollination

Fertilization

LESSON 3
REPRODUCTION

LESSON 1
MAKING AND
USING FOOD

PLANTS

LESSON 4
ADAPTATIONS AND
PROCESSES FOR
GROWTH

LESSON 2
PLANT
RESPONSES

Seed Dispersal

How Plants Use Leaves

Materials

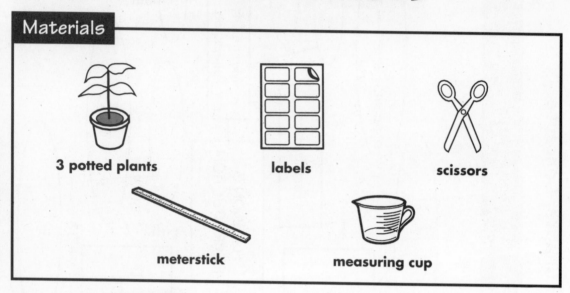

3 potted plants

labels

scissors

meterstick

measuring cup

Activity Procedure

1. Label the plants *Normal*, *Half*, and *None*.

2. Using scissors, carefully cut off all the leaves of the plant labeled *None*. Cut off half the leaves of the plant labeled *Half*. The number of leaves is the variable.

3. Don't do anything to the plant labeled *Normal*. This plant is the control.

4. Use the meterstick to **measure** the height of each plant. **Record** the heights.

5. Put all three plants in a place where they will get plenty of sunlight. Water the plants as needed. Use the measuring cup to ensure they all get the same amount of water. What do you **hypothesize** about how the plants will grow?

6. **Measure** the heights of the plants every day, and **record** your data. Record anything else you **observe** about the plants. Cut off any new leaves that grow on the plants labeled *Half* and *None*.

7. At the end of two weeks, review your data.

Harcourt

Name _____

Draw Conclusions

1. Which plant grew the most in height? Which plant grew the least? Does the data support your **hypothesis**? What can you conclude about the importance of leaves? _____

_____

_____

2. The number of leaves on each plant was the independent variable. What was the dependent variable in this investigation? _____

_____

_____

3. **Scientists at Work** Scientists always **control variables** when they **experiment**. What variables did you control in this investigation? _____

_____

_____

Investigate Further Does adding plant food really improve plant growth, as advertisements would have you believe? **Plan and conduct a simple investigation** to answer this question or another question you might have. Be sure you **control variables** in your investigation. Also be sure you write instructions others can follow in carrying out the procedure.

_____

_____

_____

_____

Harcourt

Control Variables

When you control variables, you are better able to draw valid conclusions about the data you collect in an experiment. The first step is to identify which conditions in an experiment may change the experiment's outcome. Then you control all but one of those conditions.

Think About Controlling Variables

Mary has a large pond stocked with several kinds of fish. She has been feeding the fish the same food for years, and her fish have always been healthy. Now she has found another brand of food that is less expensive. She is concerned, however, that the new brand will not be as good for her fish as the more expensive brand. To experiment, she takes water from the pond and puts the same amount into two identical aquarium tanks. She puts a few fish in each tank, making sure that each tank has the same number, kind, and size of fish. She sprinkles the old brand of fish food in one tank and the new brand in the other tank. After one week Mary sees that the fish in both tanks are still healthy. After another week all the fish are still healthy, but some of the fish eating the new brand of food have actually grown larger.

1. What are the variables in Mary's experiment? _____

   _____

   _____

   _____

2. Which of the variables did Mary deliberately change? _____

3. Mary forgot to control one other important variable. Which one was it?

   _____

4. How do you think having two uncontrolled variables will affect the

   experiment? _____

   _____

5. Other than the type of food, can you think of another variable that may

   explain why the fish got bigger in one tank? _____

   _____

   _____

   _____

Harcourt

Use with page A101.

Name _____

Date _____

How Do Plants Make Food?

Lesson Concept

Plants make food in their leaves by photosynthesis, the process in which chlorophyll uses light energy to combine water and carbon dioxide to form glucose and oxygen. Plants use most of this food and store the rest. The extra food is passed to animals that eat the plants. Plants and animals use food energy, which is released by cellular respiration.

Vocabulary

photosynthesis (A102)   **epidermis** (A102)   **palisade layer** (A103)

cellular respiration (A106)

Match each term on the left with its description on the right.

Column A

_____ 1. upper epidermis

_____ 2. glucose

_____ 3. cellular respiration

_____ 4. palisade layer

_____ 5. photosynthesis

_____ 6. guard cells

_____ 7. chlorophyll

_____ 8. chloroplasts

_____ 9. spongy layer

_____ 10. cuticle

_____ 11. veins

Column B

A a process by which plants make food

B a substance in chloroplasts that changes light energy into chemical energy

C the system of xylem and phloem tubes in leaves

D a layer of cells that lies below the palisade layer and has many air spaces

E structures that contain chlorophyll, which gives plants their green color

F a type of sugar made in leaves

G the waxy covering of the epidermis

H a layer of cells that has many chloroplasts and that lies directly below the upper epidermis

I a process by which plants release the energy in food to carry on life processes

J the single layer of protective cells on the upper surface of a leaf

K cells that form the edges of the stomata

Harcourt

How Plants Get the Light They Need

Materials

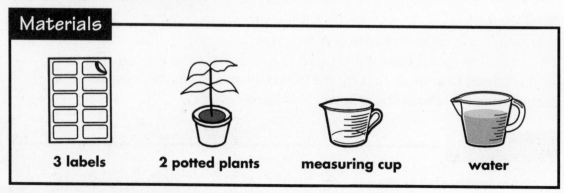

3 labels   2 potted plants   measuring cup   water

Activity Procedure

1 Write *Odd days* on one of the labels. Put the label on one side of a pot. Write *Even days* on a second label. Put this label on the other side of the same pot. Write *Don't move* on the third label, and put it on the other pot.

2 Place both potted plants in a sunny area. If you don't have a sunny area, put them under and to one side of a light source, such as a lamp. Make sure both plants are on the same side of and at the same distance from the lamp.

3 Use the measuring cup to give both plants the same amount of water at the same time each day. **Observe** the plants every day, and **record** your observations.

4 Turn the plant labeled *Odd days/Even days* one-half turn every day. If you start the **experiment** on an even-numbered day, place the pot so you can see the *Even days* label. If you start on an odd-numbered day, place the pot so that you can see the *Odd days* label. Do not turn the plant labeled *Don't move*.

5 After ten days write a summary of your **observations** about how the plants have grown. Draw pictures showing how the plants looked at the beginning and at the end of the **experiment**.

Harcourt

Name _____

Draw Conclusions

1. What did you **observe** about the growth of the plants during the investigation?

_____

_____

2. Compare the two plants. What variable were the plants responding to?

_____

3. Scientists at Work Scientists often **compare** organisms to help them understand how organisms respond to their environments. In this investigation, how did comparing the way the plants grew help you **draw conclusions** about the way plants respond to light? What other information is

needed to support your conclusions? _____

_____

_____

Investigate Further Hypothesize about all plants needing the same amount of sunlight. Try putting two different plants in a very sunny window. **Observe**, and

record your observations of the plants for two weeks. _____

_____

_____

_____

Harcourt

Name _____

Date _____

Compare and Draw Conclusions

When you draw conclusions, you use many other process skills, such as processing data collected from literature research.

Think About Comparing and Drawing Conclusions

Jason was buying grass seed for his mother's lawn. His mother wanted the grass to grow well under the maple trees, in the direct sun at the south side of the house, and in the moist shaded area at the bottom of the backyard slope. Jason went to the garden center and looked at the different types of grass seed. Each bag of seed had a description of what the grass would look like and where it would grow best. He took the following notes:

Jackson Brand: dark green, thick "carpet," grows well in shade, keep out of full sun, turns green in mid-March, goes dormant (brown) at first frost

Black Beard Grass: dark green, average thickness, grows best in moist, shaded areas, stays green all year

Wicked Weed Grass: medium green, medium thickness, needs full sun, turns green in mid-March, goes dormant at first frost

1. Fill in the chart to help in drawing conclusions.

	Jackson Brand	**Black Beard**	**Wicked Weed**
Color			
Thickness			
Needs sun or shade			
When it turns green			
When it goes dormant			

2. What conclusions can you draw from the data in the chart? _____

_____

Harcourt

Use with page A109.

Concept Review

How Do Plants Respond to Light and Gravity?

Lesson Concept

Tropisms cause plants to respond to certain stimuli, such as light and gravity. Some plants respond to touch.

Vocabulary

tropism (A110)   **phototropism** (A110)   **gravitropism** (A111)

Write a *T* in front of the true statements and an *F* in front of the false statements. If the statement is false, write a correction to it in the space provided.

_____ **1.** A plant's response to a stimulus is called a tropism. _____

_____

_____ **2.** Gravitropism is an adaptation that causes some plants to live longer

than others. _____

_____

_____ **3.** Some plants have parts that can move in response to being touched.

_____

_____ **4.** If a seed lands upside down, its roots will grow upward and may never

touch the soil. _____

_____

_____ **5.** Phototropism is a plant's response to light. _____

_____ **6.** A stimulus is anything that causes an organism to respond.

_____

_____ **7.** A plant bends toward the light, because the cells on the side of the plant

facing the light are shorter. _____

_____

Harcourt

Flower Parts

Materials

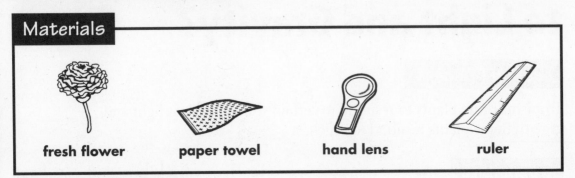

fresh flower   paper towel   hand lens   ruler

Activity Procedure

1 Place a fresh flower on a paper towel.

2 **Observe** the outside of the flower. Notice the green, leaflike parts around the petals. These are called *sepals* (SEE•puhls). How many sepals does the flower have? What shape are the sepals? **Record** your observations.

3 Now **observe** the flower's petals. How many petals does the flower have? What shape are they? What color are they? Do the petals have any patterns, or are they one color? What do the petals feel like? **Record** your observations.

4 **Observe** the flower with your eyes closed. Does it have an odor? How would you describe the odor? What part of the flower do you think the odor is coming from? **Record** your observations about the flower's odor.

5 Using the hand lens, **observe** the inside of the flower. What parts do you see? What are the shapes of these parts? **Measure** these parts. **Record** your observations about the inside of the flower.

6 Now make a drawing of the inside of the flower. As you draw each part, try to **infer** what it does.

Harcourt

Name _____

Draw Conclusions

1. Colorful markings and strong odors often attract birds and insects to flowers. How might the location of the markings and odors attract birds and insects to the flower? _____

_____

_____

_____

2. In the very center of a flower is the female reproductive part. Stalks surrounding the center contain male reproductive parts. **Infer** how it might help the plant to have the male parts around the female part.

_____

_____

_____

3. **Scientists at Work** When scientists **infer** a part's function, they sometimes base their inferences on **observing** the part's location. Based on the sepals' location, what could you infer about the function of sepals? _____

_____

_____

_____

Investigate Further Observe the parts of several kinds of flowers. How do those flowers **compare** to the one you observed in this investigation? Do they have the same number of sepals? Are the petals arranged the same way? Do the flowers' inner parts look the same? Classify the flowers based on your observations.

_____

_____

_____

Harcourt

Name _____

Date _____

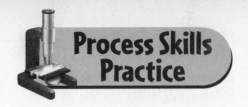

Infer

When you infer, you explain an event by using observation, previous information or experience, and your own judgment. Inferences supported by observation and reasoning are always valid, but they may not always be correct.

Think About Inferring

Tami saw an article in the newspaper about the poor apple harvest in her area. Farmers were blaming the poor harvest on the heavy rains that had fallen earlier that year. One farmer interviewed for the article said, "There was so much rain in the spring that the bees couldn't get out. Those that did go out of their hives were knocked to the ground and drowned." Tami was confused. She asked herself, "What do bees have to do with a poor apple harvest?"

1. What event was Tami trying to explain? _____

2. What observations can she use? _____

   _____

3. What previous knowledge or experience could Tami use to help her

   understand why the apple harvest was poor? _____

   _____

   _____

4. Tami tries an inference: perhaps the bees add honey to the apples to make them

   sweeter. What are some reasons this inference might be wrong? _____

   _____

   _____

5. Can you think of one inference Tami could make based on her observations

   that would be valid? _____

   _____

Name _____

Date _____

How Do Vascular Plants Reproduce Sexually?

Lesson Concept

Most flowers have both male and female reproductive parts. Pollen, which has sperm cells, is produced by the stamens. The pistil has the eggs. Pollen is transferred from the stamens to the pistil. After fertilization, the eggs develop into seeds.

Vocabulary

fertilization (A116) **stamens** (A116) **pistil** (A116) **ovary** (A117)

Answer each of the questions below by writing *yes* or *no* in the space on the left. Then, on the lines beneath the question, explain your answer.

_____ **1.** Do most flowers have only female reproductive parts? _____

_____

_____ **2.** Do the stamens have eggs? _____

_____

_____ **3.** Is pollen transferred from the pistil to the stamens? _____

_____

_____ **4.** Is the pistil the flower's female reproductive part? _____

_____

_____ **5.** Do animals carry eggs from one flower to another? _____

_____

_____ **6.** Do some plants depend on the wind to transfer pollen? _____

_____

_____ **7.** Do gymnosperms have flowers? _____

_____

Harcourt

Name _____

Date _____

Investigate Log

The Parts of a Seed

Materials

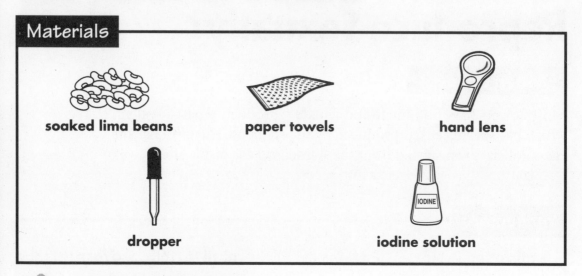

soaked lima beans   paper towels   hand lens

dropper   iodine solution

CAUTION ## Activity Procedure

1. Put a soaked lima bean on a paper towel. **Observe** the seed with the hand lens. **Record** your observations by drawing a picture of what you see.

2. Carefully peel away the outer covering of the bean. This covering is called the *seed coat.*

3. Gently open the bean by splitting it in half. Use the hand lens to **observe** the parts inside the bean. **Record** your observations by drawing a picture of what you see.

4. Using the point of a pencil, carefully remove the part of the bean that looks like a tiny plant. This is called the *embryo.* Look through the hand lens to identify the parts of the embryo that look like leaves, a stem, and a root.

5. **CAUTION** **Iodine can stain your hands and clothes.** Carefully, put a drop or two of the iodine solution on the other parts of the bean. These parts are called the *cotyledons.* **Observe** what happens. **Record** your observations.

6. Label the seed coat, embryo, and cotyledons on your drawing from Step 3. On the embryo, label the parts that look like leaves, a stem, and a root.

Harcourt

Name _____

Draw Conclusions

1. What words would you use to describe the seed coat of the bean? What do you **infer** is its function? _____

_____

_____

2. Iodine turns black in the presence of starch, a kind of food that plants store. Because of this, what do you **infer** is the function of the cotyledons?

_____

_____

3. **Scientists at Work** Scientists **observe** many plant parts. They often **communicate** to other scientists inferences they have made about the functions of certain parts. They use descriptions, data tables, graphs, and drawings. Write a report to communicate to a classmate your inferences and conclusions about the function of cotyledons. Be sure to include the results of the iodine test.

_____

_____

_____

Investigate Further **Observe** other seeds that can be easily opened, such as green peas, squash seeds, or watermelon seeds. **Compare** them to the bean seed in this investigation. _____

_____

_____

_____

Name _____

Date _____

Communicate

When you communicate, you give information. In science you communicate by showing results from an activity in an organized way, such as by using a chart. Then you and other people can interpret the results.

Think About Communicating

Richard was working in his basement laboratory every night. He was trying to invent a new kind of glue that would stick to almost everything but would not be poisonous. He decided to use only things that you can eat. He mixed flour with water. It was a good glue, but Richard was sure he could do better. So he mixed corn starch with milk and grape jelly. That was good, too, but he wanted to see if he could do even better. After several weeks in his laboratory, he had still not invented the glue he was looking for. He called his friend Jefferson, who was working on the same problem in his own basement laboratory. Jefferson asked him which formula he had been working on. Richard realized then that he couldn't say exactly.

1. What information should Richard have recorded while he was working in his laboratory? _____

_____

2. Why should Richard have kept better records? _____

_____

_____

3. What would be a good method for keeping track of what Richard had tried?

_____

_____

4. How could Richard be sure he had communicated his information well?

_____

5. Can you think of any other way effective communication might have made Richard's experimentation easier? _____

_____

_____

_____

Harcourt

Name _____

Date _____

How Do Plants Grow?

Lesson Concept

Seeds contain embryo plants and stored food. Under the right conditions, seeds germinate. Seedlings are young plants that grow from the embryos. Some plants may reproduce asexually through vegetative propagation. Farmers and scientists use cross-pollination and grafting as other means of plant reproduction.

Vocabulary

embryo (A122)   **cotyledons** (A122)   **germinate** (A124)

seedling (A124)   **vegetative propagation** (A125)   **grafting** (A126)

tissue culture (A126)

The following boxes make up a flowchart showing how a plant grows. Below the boxes you will find captions describing each part of the growth process. Put the letter of the correct caption in each box of the flowchart.

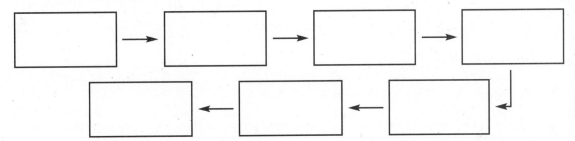

A As the root gets longer and thicker, a stem begins to emerge.

B Landing on moist, warm, fertile soil will allow the seed to take in moisture, to swell, and to germinate.

C The seed contains an embryo and stored food.

D The first part to emerge from the seed is the root.

E The seedling cannot yet make its own food but uses food stored in its cotyledons to grow.

F The seedling now has a well-developed root system, and its first leaves are producing food.

G The seed is dispersed by animals, wind, or water.

Harcourt

Recognize Vocabulary

Listed below are scrambled vocabulary terms from Chapter 4. Use the clues to unscramble the terms. Write the unscrambled terms on the lines provided.

1. PIPOOSTORMTH

_____

a plant's response to light

2. PRECLURELINARSATOIL
(2 words)

_____

the process by which plants release energy in food to carry on life processes

3. FRANGITG

_____

a form of artificial reproduction that involves attaching branches from one plant to the branches of another plant

4. CEDOSTLOYN

_____

structures inside a seed that store food

5. ZELNITARITIOF

_____

the joining of a male reproductive cell with a female reproductive cell

6. EMISPIDER

_____

the single layer of cells on the surface of a leaf

7. AGREMETIN

_____

sprout

8. INSLEGED

_____

an embryo plant that has emerged from its seed and that is using energy from its cotyledons to grow

9. EMANSTS

_____

the parts of a flower that produce pollen

10. HISPETHONSOYTS

_____

the process by which plants make food

11. EVAPORATIONGIVETEPAGT
(2 words)

_____

the ability of some plants to reproduce without seeds

Harcourt

Chapter 1 • Graphic Organizer for Chapter Concepts

Earth's Air and Water

LESSON 1
WHAT MAKES UP EARTH'S ATMOSPHERE?

Air Has Properties

1. _____
2. _____
3. _____

The Atmosphere Has Layers

4. _____
5. _____
6. _____
7. _____

LESSON 2
HOW ARE ATMOSPHERIC CONDITIONS MEASURED?

You measure

1. Temperature with a _____.

2. Humidity with a _____.

3. Precipitation with a _____.

4. Air pressure with a _____.

5. Wind speed with an _____.

6. Wind direction with a _____.

LESSON 3
WHAT ROLE DO OCEANS PLAY IN THE WATER CYCLE?

1. First, the sun _____ ocean water.

2. Then, the water vapor rises and _____ into clouds.

3. Then, fresh water falls from clouds as _____.

LESSON 4
WHY IS THE WATER CYCLE IMPORTANT?

We need fresh water for

1. _____
2. _____
3. bathing
4. sanitation
5. _____
6. _____

Name _____

Date _____

A Property of Air

Materials

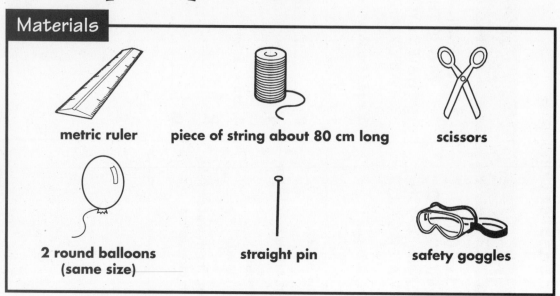

metric ruler

piece of string about 80 cm long

scissors

2 round balloons (same size)

straight pin

safety goggles

Activity Procedure

1 Work with a partner. Use the scissors to carefully cut the string into three equal pieces. **CAUTION** Be careful when using scissors.

2 Tie one piece of the string to the middle of the ruler.

3 Blow up the balloons so they are about the same size. Seal the balloons. Then tie a piece of string around the neck of each balloon.

4 Tie a balloon to each end of the ruler. Hold the middle string up so that the ruler hangs from it. Move the strings so that the ruler is balanced.

5 **CAUTION** Put on your safety goggles. Use the straight pin to pop one of the balloons. **Observe** what happens to the ruler.

My observations: _____

_____

_____

Harcourt

Name _____

Draw Conclusions

1. Explain how this investigation shows that air takes up space.

   _____

   _____

2. Describe what happened when one balloon was popped. What property
   of air caused what you **observed**? _____

   _____

   _____

3. **Scientists at Work** Scientists often **infer** conclusions when the answer to
   a question is not clear or can't be **observed** directly. Your breath is invisible, but
   you observed how it made the balloons and the ruler behave. Even though you
   can't see air, what can you infer about whether or not air is matter? Explain.

   _____

   _____

   _____

   _____

   Investigate Further What other questions do you have about air? **Plan and
   conduct a simple investigation** to answer one of your questions. Write
   instructions that others can follow to carry out the procedure.

   _____

   _____

   _____

Harcourt

Name _____

Date _____

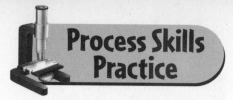

Observe and Infer

You make observations when you notice details. You make inferences when you use those details to come up with a possible explanation for why or how an event occurred.

Think About Observing and Inferring

Martha crumpled several pieces of paper and stuffed them into the bottom of a drinking glass. She pushed the glass straight down into a bowl of water. She held the glass down for one minute. During that minute nothing happened. The paper stayed where it was in the glass, and no bubbles rose to the surface of the water. Then Martha pulled the glass straight out of the water. She pulled the paper out of the bottom of the drinking glass. The paper and the inside of the glass were dry.

1. Fill in the table below with observations Martha made.

When Observation Was Made	Observation
Before the experiment	
During the experiment	
During the experiment	
After the experiment	

2. What inferences might Martha make from her observations? _____

_____

_____

_____

_____

Harcourt

Name _____

Date _____

What Makes Up Earth's Atmosphere?

Lesson Concept

Earth is surrounded by four thin layers of air called the atmosphere.

Vocabulary

atmosphere (B6) **air pressure** (B7) **troposphere** (B8) **stratosphere** (B8)

Answer the questions below.

1. Describe how the atmosphere formed and changed over time. _____

_____

_____

_____

2. What does carbon dioxide in the atmosphere do? _____

_____

Label the diagram of the atmosphere, and describe each layer. In your descriptions, tell where the air pressure is highest and where it is lowest, where the temperature is highest and lowest, and where the ozone layer is.

3. Layer: _____

Description: _____

_____

4. Layer: _____

Description: _____

_____

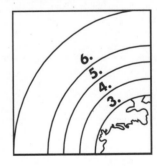

5. Layer: _____

Description: _____

_____

_____

6. Layer: _____

Description: _____

_____

_____

Harcourt

Use with page B9.

Name _____

Date _____

Measuring Atmospheric Conditions

Materials

weather station

Activity Procedure

1. Use the Weather Station Daily Record chart below to **record** the date, the time, the temperature, the amount of rain or snow, the wind direction and speed, and the cloud conditions each day for five days. Try to **record** the weather conditions at the same time each day.

2. Place the weather station in a shady spot, 1 m above the ground. **Record** the temperature.

3. Be sure the rain gauge will not collect runoff from any buildings or trees. **Record** the amount of rain or snow (if any).

4. Be sure the wind vane is located where wind from any direction will reach it. **Record** the wind direction and speed. Winds are labeled with the direction from which they blow.

Weather Station Daily Record					
Date					
Time					
Temperature					
Rainfall or snowfall					
Wind direction and speed					
Cloud condition					

Harcourt

Name _____

5 Describe and **record** the cloud conditions by noting how much of the sky is covered by clouds. Draw a circle and shade in the part of the circle that equals the amount of sky covered with clouds.

6 Use the temperature data to make a line graph showing how the temperature changes from day to day.

Draw Conclusions

1. Use your Weather Station Daily Record to **compare** the atmospheric conditions on two different days. _____

_____

_____

_____

2. From the **data** you **gathered** in this activity, how might scientists use this data to **predict** the weather? _____

_____

_____

_____

3. **Scientists at Work** Scientists learn about the weather by **measuring** atmospheric conditions and **gathering data** from other sources. What could you infer by measuring the amount of rain your area received during the week?

_____

_____

_____

Investigate Further Newspaper and television weather reports usually describe the sky or cloud conditions as sunny, mostly sunny, partly sunny, partly cloudy, mostly cloudy, or cloudy. Using the data from your table, **classify** each day's cloud conditions as if you were writing a newspaper report. _____

_____

_____

_____

Harcourt

Name _____

Date _____

Measure and Gather Data

Measurements are a kind of observation. You measure when you use a tool, such as a thermometer, a clock, or a ruler.

Think About Measuring and Gathering Data

When you measure, you are actually comparing. For example, if you measure a rope and find that the rope is 1.5 m long, you are comparing the length of the rope to a standard length. The standard is, in this case, the meter. If you weigh the rope and find that it weighs 20 newtons, you are comparing the rope to a standard weight, the newton. Of course, it's important to use the right measuring unit, too. For example, you wouldn't measure a 5-m rope in kilometers. You would use meters. Think about setting new standards for measuring lengths, as shown below.

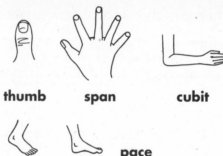

thumb   span   cubit

pace

1. Which of these units would you use to measure the length of a swimming pool?

_____

2. Which would you use to measure your height? _____

_____

3. How many spans equal a cubit? _____

_____

4. Why do you think no one uses a measuring system like this one?

_____

_____

_____

5. How could you make this measuring system work as a standard?

_____

_____

Harcourt

Concept Review

How Are Atmospheric Conditions Measured?

Lesson Concept

Weather conditions such as temperature, air pressure, humidity, wind speed and direction, and precipitation can be observed and measured.

Vocabulary

weather (B12)	**humidity** (B13)	**precipitation** (B13)
evaporation (B15)	**condensation** (B15)	**water cycle** (B15)

Answer each question with one or more complete sentences.

1. Where in the atmosphere does most weather occur? _____

_____

2. Why does most weather occur only in one layer of the atmosphere?

_____

_____

_____

3. What is the largest source of water for the water cycle? _____

_____

4. Fog is actually a cloud that is low enough to touch the ground. What kind of

cloud is fog? _____

5. What are you measuring when you measure air pressure? _____

_____

6. Why do people measure atmospheric conditions? _____

_____

7. If you see cumulus clouds in the sky, what type of weather are you likely to

have? _____

_____

Harcourt

Getting Fresh Water from Salt Water

Materials

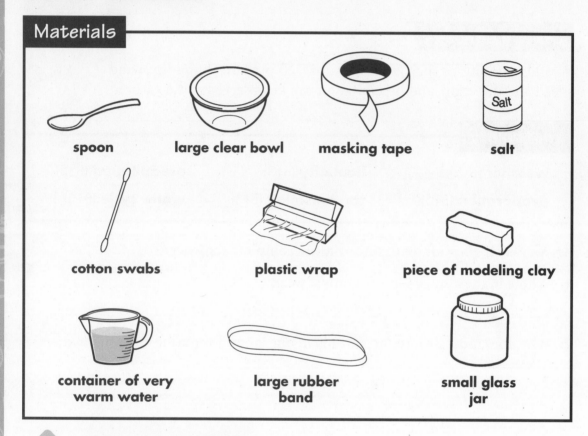

spoon	large clear bowl	masking tape	salt
cotton swabs	plastic wrap		piece of modeling clay
container of very warm water	large rubber band		small glass jar

CAUTION Activity Procedure

❶ Stir two spoonfuls of salt into the container of very warm water. Put one end of a clean cotton swab into this mixture. Taste the mixture by touching the swab to your tongue. **Record** your **observations. CAUTION** Don't share swabs. Don't put a swab that has touched your mouth back into any substance. Never taste anything in an investigation or experiment unless you are told to do so.

My observations: _____

_____

❷ Pour the salt water into the large bowl. Put the jar in the center of the bowl of salt water.

❸ Put the plastic wrap over the top of the bowl. The wrap should not touch the top of the jar inside the bowl. Put a large rubber band around the bowl to

Harcourt

Name _____

hold the wrap in place.

4 Form the clay into a small ball. Put the ball on top of the plastic wrap right over the jar. Make sure the plastic wrap doesn't touch the jar.

5 On the outside of the bowl, use tape to mark the level of the salt water. Place the bowl in a sunny spot for one day.

6 After one day, remove the plastic wrap and the clay ball. Use clean swabs to taste the water in the jar and in the bowl. **Record** your **observations**.

My observations: _____

_____

Draw Conclusions

1. What did you **observe** by using your sense of taste? _____

_____

_____

2. What do you **infer** happened to the salt water? _____

_____

3. Scientists at Work The movement of water from the Earth's surface, through the atmosphere, and back to Earth's surface is called the water cycle. From what you **observed,** what can you **infer** about the ocean's role in the water cycle?

_____

_____

_____

Investigate Further Put the plastic wrap and the clay back on the large bowl. Leave the bowl in the sun until the water in the large bowl is gone. **Observe** the bowl and the jar. What can you conclude about the water that evaporates from ocean water? What other information do you need to support your conclusions?

_____

_____

_____

_____

Harcourt

Observe and Infer

You use your senses to make observations. You use these observations to make inferences, which are explanations or opinions, about what you have observed.

Think About Observing and Inferring

Eugene wanted to demonstrate to his friends that different bodies of water contain different amounts of salts. He found a table that showed the amount of salt dissolved in the water from lakes and oceans in different parts of the world. He used the table to help mix samples of water with varying salinity. Then he asked his friends to taste his samples and rate them for saltiness.

Ranking (Least Salty to Most Salty)	Sample
1	E
2	A
3	D
4	F
5	B
6	C

Body of Water	Salinity	Sample
Atlantic Ocean	35 g/1000 g	
Arctic Ocean	31 g/1000 g	
Black Sea	15 g/1000 g	
Dead Sea	300 g/1000 g	
Great Salt Lake	200 g/1000 g	
Lake Superior	<1g/1000 g	

1. The table on the left gives the ranking of the samples by Eugene's friends. Which sample did they rank the most salty? Which sample did they rank the least salty?

_____

2. The table on the right gives the salinity of different bodies of water. Based on the table above, infer which of the samples corresponds to which body of water. Then, fill in the right column of the table.

3. Eugene told his friends that they made an error in their ranking. He said that Sample D was actually saltier than Sample F. Do you think his friends were

   careless in their work? Explain your answer. _____

_____

Use with page B19.

Harcourt

What Role Do Oceans Play in the Water Cycle?

Lesson Concept

The interactions between the oceans, other bodies of water, the sun, and the land cause the recycling of most of Earth's water.

Define the following terms, and show where each occurs in the diagram of the water cycle.

1. Evaporation: _____

_____

2. Condensation: _____

_____

3. Precipitation: _____

_____

_____

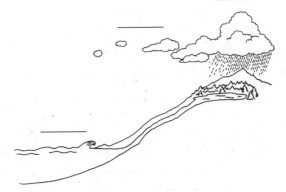

For each of the places listed, say whether the ocean water is saltier than average, of average saltiness, or less salty than average.

4. _____ in the middle of a large ocean

5. _____ near the North Pole

6. _____ near the equator

7. _____ where a river flows into the ocean

Harcourt

Water, Water Everywhere

Materials

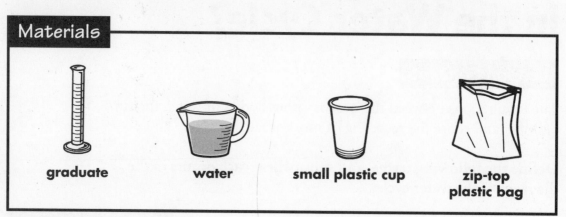

graduate   water   small plastic cup   zip-top
                                                             plastic bag

Activity Procedure

1 Using the graduate, **measure** and pour 100 mL of water into the cup.

2 Open the plastic bag, and carefully put the cup inside. Then seal the bag. Be careful not to spill any water from the cup.

3 Place the sealed bag near a sunny window. **Predict** what will happen to the water in the cup.

My prediction: _____

4 Leave the bag near a window for 3–4 days. **Observe** the cup and the bag each day. **Record** what you see.

My observation: _____

_____

5 Remove the cup from the bag. **Measure** the amount of water in the cup by pouring it back into the graduate. **Calculate** any difference in the amount of water you poured into the cup and the amount of water you removed from the cup.

My measurement: _____

My calculation: _____

Harcourt

Draw Conclusions

1. What did you **observe** during the time the cup was inside the bag?

_____

2. Where do you think the water in the bag came from? Explain.

_____

_____

3. Scientists at Work Scientists often **infer** the cause of something they **observe**. What can you infer about the amount of water in the bag? _____

_____

Investigate Further Develop a testable question about where the missing water went. Decide what equipment you will need, and then **plan and carry out a simple investigation** that will help you answer your question. Be sure to write instructions so that others can follow your procedure.

My hypothesis: _____

_____

My investigation plan: _____

_____

_____

My results: _____

Harcourt

Infer

When you infer, you draw conclusions to explain events.
Your inferences may not always be correct.

Think About Inferring

1. Dion lives in a town with a lake nearby. People use the lake to swim, fish, and go boating. Dion read in the newspaper that the rainfall in the area had been less than normal for the summer. When he went to the lake, he noticed that the water level in the lake was lower than usual for the time of year. What could Dion infer caused the water level in the lake to be below normal?

   _____

   _____

2. Since there had been little rain in Dion's town, people were told not to water their lawns. Many plants in Dion's yard and garden turned brown and died. But the big trees were still green and leafy. What could Dion infer caused some

   plants to die and the trees to survive? _____

   _____

   _____

3. Last year Dion's uncle Jeb had a house built outside Dion's town. Jeb built a deep well to pull water up into his house. This year Jeb was not able to get any water from his well. What could Jeb infer caused him not to get water from his

   well this year? _____

   _____

4. Jeb found out that he needs to dig his well deeper to get water. The county engineer explained to Jeb that many people built houses and drilled wells near Jeb. This caused the groundwater level to drop several feet when everyone started using their wells. The county engineer also told Jeb that his ground-water comes from an underground river. The lack of rain during the summer would not affect the groundwater level. Knowing this, tell whether your

   inference was correct in Question 3. _____

5. What does Question 4 show you about making inferences? _____

   _____

   _____

Harcourt

Why Is the Water Cycle Important?

Lesson Concept

The water cycle provides Earth with a constant supply of fresh water, a limited resource that plants and animals need. Human activities such as manufacturing and farming can pollute fresh water supplies. Because of its importance, people must conserve fresh water and keep it clean.

Vocabulary

transpiration (B27)

Underline the best answer.

1. Earth's water moves through the environment in the ____.

   A ocean   **B** water cycle   **C** precipitation   **D** evaporation

2. Most of the Earth's water is unavailable to humans because it is ____ water.

   A fresh   **B** ice   **C** salt   **D** gaseous

3. Plants give off water to the air through ____.

   A transpiration   **B** condensation   **C** transportation   **D** precipitation

4. Less than one percent of Earth's fresh water can be used because most fresh water is ____.

   A liquid   **B** salty   **C** frozen   **D** polluted

5. People use fresh water for manufacturing, farming, bathing, and getting rid of waste. These activities can ____ the water.

   A clean   **B** condense   **C** pollute   **D** recycle

6. Rainwater can carry harmful chemicals into the soil. The chemicals can seep from the soil into ____.

   A groundwater   **B** oceans   **C** glaciers   **D** clouds

7. It is important to keep pollution out of the soil, because groundwater supplies water for crops and ____.

   A drinking   **B** ice   **C** recreation   **D** transportation

Harcourt

Recognize Vocabulary

In the space provided, write the letter of the word in Column B
that best fits the definition in Column A. Use each word only once.

Column A

_____ 1. Layer of the atmosphere that contains
ozone

_____ 2. Layer of air that surrounds Earth

_____ 3. Process in which water vapor changes into
liquid drops of water

_____ 4. Condition of the atmosphere at any moment

_____ 5. Transferring of water from Earth's surface
to the atmosphere and back

_____ 6. Weight of particles of air pressing down
on Earth

_____ 7. Process in which liquid water changes into
water vapor

_____ 8. Process in which plants release water
through stomata

_____ 9. Layer of the atmosphere closest to
Earth's surface

_____ 10. Rain, snow, sleet, or hail

_____ 11. Water in the air

Column B

A troposphere

B humidity

C atmosphere

D stratosphere

E transpiration

F air pressure

G condensation

H precipitation

I evaporation

J water cycle

K weather

Harcourt

Harcourt

Chapter 2 • Graphic Organizer for Chapter Concepts

Earth's Weather

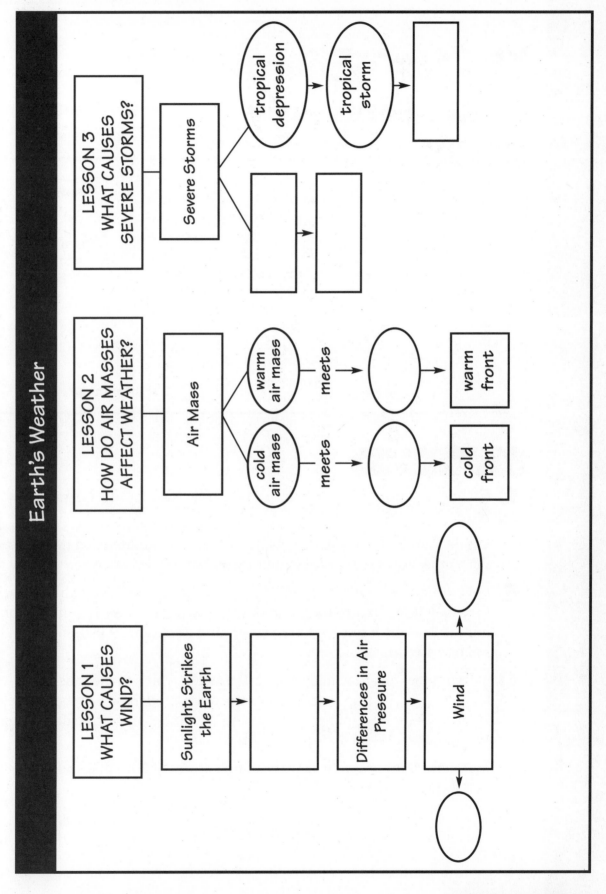

Name _____

Date _____

The Sun's Energy Heats Unevenly

Materials

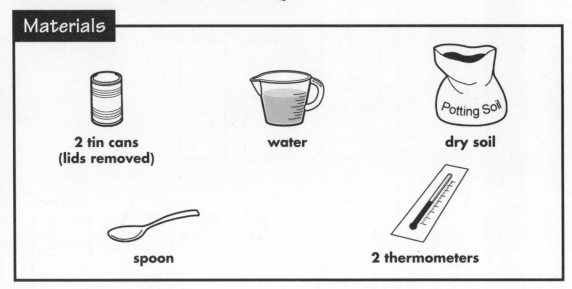

2 tin cans
(lids removed)

water

dry soil

spoon

2 thermometers

Activity Procedure

1. Fill one can about $\frac{3}{4}$ full of water and the other can about $\frac{3}{4}$ full of soil.

2. Place one thermometer in the can of water and the other in the can of soil. Put the cans in a shady place outside. Wait for 10 minutes, and then **record** the temperatures of the water and the soil.

3. Put both cans in sunlight. **Predict** which of the cans will show the faster rise in temperature. **Record** the temperature of each can every 10 minutes for 30 minutes. In which can does the temperature rise faster? Which material— soil or water—heats up faster?

4. Now put the cans back in the shade. **Predict** in which of the cans the temperature will drop faster. Again **record** the temperature of each can every 10 minutes for 30 minutes. In which can does the temperature drop faster? Which material—soil or water—cools off faster?

5. Make line graphs to show how the temperatures of both materials changed as they heated up and cooled off.

Harcourt

Name _____

Draw Conclusions

1. What was the dependent variable in this investigation? What independent variables did you test? _____

   _____

   _____

2. From the results you graphed in this investigation, which would you **predict** heats up faster—ocean or land? Which would you predict cools off faster? Explain. _____

   _____

   _____

3. **Scientists at Work** Scientists learn by **predicting** and then testing their predictions. How did you test your predictions about water and soil? What variables did you control? _____

   _____

   _____

   _____

Investigate Further Predict how fast other materials, such as moist soil, sand, and salt water, heat up and cool off. **Plan and conduct a simple investigation** to test your predictions. Then write a report of your investigation that includes tests conducted, data collected, and conclusions drawn. _____

_____

_____

_____

_____

Harcourt

Name _____

Date _____

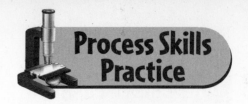

Predict

When you predict, you make a statement about what you think will happen. To make a prediction, you think about what you've observed before. You also think about how to interpret data you have.

Think About Predicting

Robert wanted to see if he could predict the weather if he knew which way the wind was blowing and whether the barometer was rising or falling. He decided to find out. All through the winter, he kept records of wind direction, air pressure, and the weather that followed his observations. Then he made this chart.

Wind Direction (From)	Barometer	Weather
varies	neither rising nor falling	pleasant weather, no changes in temperature
south, changing to southeast	falling	wind picks up, rain after a few hours
southeast, changing to northeast	falling	windy and colder
east, changing to northeast	falling slowly	rain the next day
east, changing to northeast	falling rapidly	wind increases, and it snows
south, changing to southwest	rising slowly	the skies clear, and the sun comes out
southwest, changing to west	rising rapidly	the skies clear, and it gets really cold

1. Using Robert's chart, what kind of weather would you predict if the wind is from the southwest and the barometer is neither rising nor falling?

    _____

2. Using Robert's chart, what kind of weather would you predict if the barometer is rising and the wind direction has changed from the south to the southwest?

    _____

3. The wind direction has changed from the east to the northeast, and the barometer is falling fast. Using Robert's chart, what kind of weather would you predict?

    _____

Harcourt

Use with page B39.

What Causes Wind?

Lesson Concept

Changes in air pressure, caused by uneven heating of Earth's surface and the air above it, cause the wind to blow. There are local winds and prevailing winds.

Vocabulary

local winds (B41)	prevailing winds (B41)

You know that weather conditions are caused by factors like temperature, humidity, and air pressure. The combinations of these factors form weather systems. A weather system can be a storm, very cold air, or pleasant, sunny weather. Weather systems are moved by prevailing winds from west to east across the United States.

1. Suppose weather conditions in your area are hot and dry. Do you think local winds are blowing toward the center of the hot area or away from it?

   Explain. _____

   _____

   _____

2. In which general direction is the hot and dry air mass in Question 1 most likely

   to move? Why? _____

   _____

3. Suppose it is raining today in Ohio and Michigan. What kind of weather might

   you expect to find in New York state tomorrow? _____

4. What causes prevailing winds? _____

   _____

Harcourt

Name _____

Date _____

Investigate Log

Wind Speed

Materials

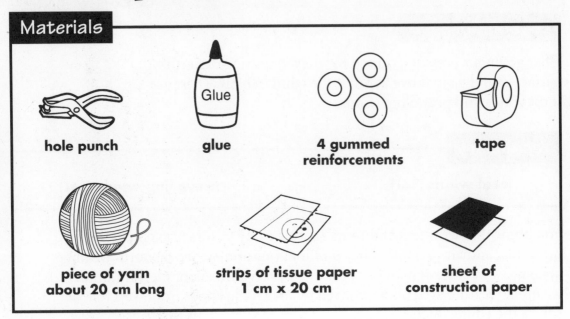

hole punch

glue

4 gummed reinforcements

tape

piece of yarn about 20 cm long

strips of tissue paper 1 cm x 20 cm

sheet of construction paper

Activity Procedure

1 Form a cylinder with the sheet of construction paper. Tape the edge of the paper to keep the cylinder from opening.

2 Use the hole punch to make two holes at one end of the cylinder. Punch them on opposite sides of the cylinder and about 3 cm from the end. Put two gummed reinforcements on each hole, one on the inside and one on the outside.

3 Thread the yarn through the holes, and tie it tightly to form a handle loop.

4 Glue strips of tissue paper to the other end of the cylinder. Put tape over the glued strips to hold them better. Your completed windsock should look like the one shown in Picture B on page B45 of your textbook.

5 Hang your windsock outside. Use the chart on the next page to **measure** wind speed each day for several days. **Record** your measurements in a chart. Include the date, time of day, observations of objects affected by the wind, and the approximate wind speed.

Harcourt

Name _____

WB89

Wind Scale			
Speed in km/hr	**Description**	**Observations on Land**	**Windsock Position**
0	no breeze	no movement of wind	limp
6–19	light breeze	leaves rustle, wind vanes move, wind felt on face	slightly up
20–38	moderate breeze	dust and paper blow, small branches sway	nearly 90 degrees to arm
39–49	strong breeze	umbrellas hard to open, large branches sway	stiff and 90 degrees from arm

Draw Conclusions

1. How fast was the weakest wind you **measured**? _____

_____

_____

How fast was the strongest wind? _____

2. How did you determine the speed of the wind? _____

_____

_____

3. Scientists at Work *Light, moderate,* and *strong* are adjectives describing wind speed. Scientists often use **measurements** to describe things because, in science, numbers are more exact than words. What do you infer the wind

speed to be if the wind is making large tree branches sway? _____

Investigate Further Determine which direction is north. **Measure** both wind speed and direction each day for a week. **Record** your data in a chart.

_____

_____

Harcourt

Process Skills Practice

Measure

Reading measurements allows you to communicate precise information about an event.

Think About Measuring

Hurricanes are powerful storms that form near the equator over warm ocean water that is at least 27°C (81°F). In the Northern Hemisphere, hurricane winds blow in a counterclockwise direction. In the Southern Hemisphere, hurricane winds blow in a clockwise direction. To be classified as a hurricane, the winds must blow at least 119 km/hr. A hurricane swirls around an area of low air pressure. The eye of the storm is a calm region at the center of the hurricane that has the lowest air pressure and generally the highest air temperatures.

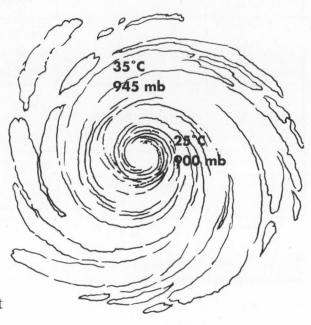

35°C
945 mb

25°C
900 mb

1. Normal air pressure is 985 millibars. What is the difference (in millibars) between the air pressure in the eye of the storm and normal air pressure?

_____

2. What is the temperature difference between the eye of the storm and the main

   body of the storm? _____

3. Imagine the storm is traveling toward a coastal city 100 kilometers away at 10 km/hr. How long would it take the storm to reach the city? Show how you

   figured this out. _____

4. Which hemisphere could this storm form in? Explain your answer.

_____

_____

Harcourt

How Do Air Masses Affect Weather?

Lesson Concept

The sun warms Earth unevenly, forming air masses of different temperatures.

Vocabulary

air mass (B46)   front (B47)

Fill in the blanks below by describing what happens to the sun's radiation.

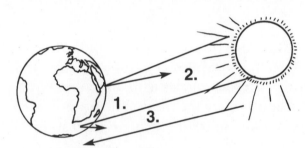

1. _____

2. _____

3. _____

Label the key for the weather map.

Key

4. _____

5. _____

6. _____

7. _____

8. Describe a warm front, and tell what happens as a warm front moves through

an area. _____

_____

_____

_____

Harcourt

Tracking Hurricanes

Materials

hurricane
tracking chart

history table for
Hurricane Zelda

3 different colored
pencils or markers

current advisory for
Hurricane Zelda

Activity Procedure

1 On the hurricane tracking chart, plot the path taken by Hurricane Zelda. Use the data from the history table and the current advisory. On the tracking chart, draw a small circle for each location listed on the history table. Use an ordinary pencil for this step.

2 Your first circles show Zelda as a tropical depression. When winds exceed 39 miles per hour, a tropical depression is classified as a tropical storm and is given a name. Fill in the tropical depression circles with one color. Write *Tropical Storm Zelda* under the location where the tropical depression first becomes a tropical storm. Choose a different color for the tropical storm circles.

3 When winds exceed 74 miles per hour, a tropical storm becomes a hurricane. Write *Hurricane Zelda* under the location where Zelda first reaches hurricane strength. Use the color for the tropical storm to fill in all the circles from the one labeled in Step 2 to the one labeled here. Choose a different color for the hurricane circles, and fill in all of those.

Harcourt

History of Hurricane Zelda

Date and Time	Latitude	Longitude	Maximum Wind Speed
07/27 3:00 UT	23.0° N	66.0° W	35 mi. per hr.
07/27 9:00 UT	23.5° N	67.0° W	35 mi. per hr.
07/27 15:00 UT	24.0° N	67.5° W	40 mi. per hr.
07/27 21:00 UT	24.5° N	67.5° W	45 mi. per hr.
07/28 3:00 UT	25.5° N	69.0° W	55 mi. per hr.
07/28 9:00 UT	27.0° N	72.0° W	60 mi. per hr.
07/28 15:00 UT	29.0° N	72.5° W	70 mi. per hr.
07/28 21:00 UT	31.0° N	73.0° W	75 mi. per hr.
07/29 3:00 UT	31.0° N	76.0° W	85 mi. per hr.

Draw Conclusions

1. Look at the track of the storm on the map. What general patterns can you **infer** in the storm's direction and wind speed? _____

_____

_____

_____

2. Use the tracking chart and the latest data on Zelda's speed and direction to **predict** where and when the storm will strike the coast.

_____

_____

_____

3. Scientists at Work Scientists who track hurricanes often **predict** using probabilities. They list the probability of a storm's striking a spot on the coast as low, medium, or high. To which parts of the coastline would you give low, medium, and high probabilities of being hit by Hurricane Zelda?

_____

_____

_____

Harcourt

Name _____

Date _____

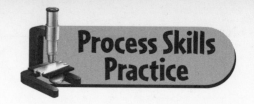

Predict

Predicting is anticipating outcomes based on your observations and inferences and on your information about past events. Good predictions are based on careful interpretation of current data and knowledge of the outcomes of similar situations in the past.

Think About Predicting

You studied Hurricane Zelda in the investigation for this lesson. Assume that Zelda actually makes landfall at Charleston as predicted. Even though the eye of the hurricane misses Cape Hatteras, Cape Hatteras still feels some effects. Use your observations of Zelda and your knowledge of the structure of a hurricane to predict the weather at Cape Hatteras.

1. What do you need to know about hurricanes to help you predict what will

   happen at Cape Hatteras? _____

   _____

   _____

   _____

2. What weather can the people of Cape Hatteras expect? _____

   _____

3. What is the value of being able to predict the effect of Hurricane Zelda on

   Cape Hatteras? _____

   _____

   _____

4. A hurricane's source of energy is the warm ocean water over which it forms
   and develops. What do you think will happen when Hurricane Zelda moves

   inland from Charleston? _____

   _____

   _____

5. What do you think would happen if Hurricane Zelda went back out to sea?

   _____

   _____

    Use with page B51.

Name _____

Date _____

What Causes Severe Storms?

Lesson Concept

Thunderstorms often form as cold fronts move into areas of warm, humid air. Hurricanes are large, spiraling storms with high winds and heavy rains. Tornadoes can form in thunderstorms and hurricanes.

Vocabulary

thunderstorm (B52) **hurricane** (B54) **tropical storm** (B54) **tornado** (B56)

Answer each question with one or more complete sentences.

1. What happens at the start of all severe thunderstorms? _____

_____

2. Describe the three stages of a thunderstorm. _____

_____

_____

_____

3. What are lightning and thunder? _____

_____

_____

_____

4. Describe the development, progression, and death of a hurricane.

_____

_____

_____

_____

_____

_____

5. If you are inside when a tornado approaches, what should you do?

_____

Harcourt

Name _____

Date _____

Recognize Vocabulary

Use the clues below to complete the word puzzle.

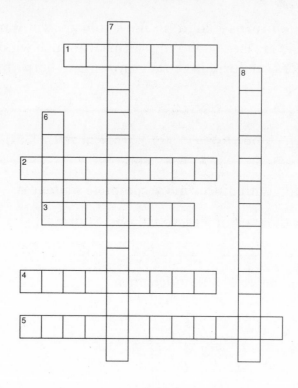

Across

1. a large body of air with the same general properties as the land over which it forms (2 words)

2. a wind that depends on local temperature changes (2 words)

3. an intense, funnel-shaped windstorm that can form within a severe thunderstorm

4. a large spiraling storm system that can be hundreds of kilometers across

5. a very strong storm with lots of rain, thunder, and lightning

Down

6. a border where two air masses meet

7. global winds that blow constantly from the same direction (2 words)

8. a spiraling storm with winds between 63 kilometers per hour (39 mi/hr) and 119 kilometers per hour (74 mi/hr) (2 words)

Harcourt

Chapter 3 • Graphic Organizer for Chapter Concepts

Weather Prediction and Climate

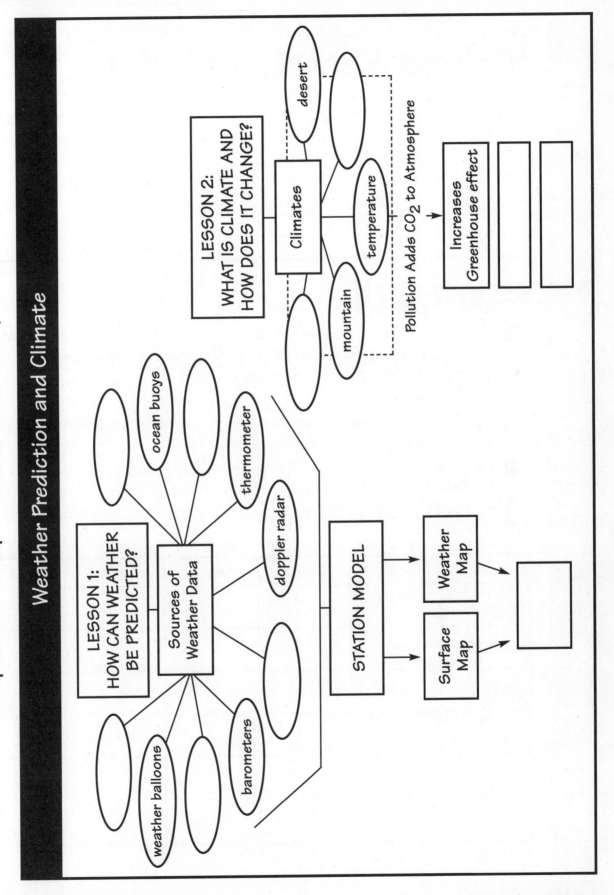

Harcourt

Name _____

Date _____

 **Investigate Log**

Making a Station Model

Materials

✓ ✓ ✓

✳✳ ○○

weather station

Activity Procedure

1 Using the weather station or other appropriate tools, **measure** and **record** the current weather conditions in the table below. Include temperature, air pressure, wind speed and direction, amount of precipitation, and cloud cover.

2 Use symbols from the table on page B66 to **record** your station model for four days in the chart below.

3 Use your observations to predict what the weather for Day 5 will be like. Record your prediction in the box for Day 5. Record the actual weather for Day 5.

	Day 1	Day 2	Day 3	Day 4	Day 5
Temperature					
Air pressure					
Wind speed					
Wind direction					
Amount of precipitation					
Cloud cover					

Harcourt

Investigate Log

Draw Conclusions

1. How did the station-model symbols help you summarize and **record data**?

_____

_____

_____

2. How did making station models for four days give you information to **predict** the weather? What other information do you infer might be useful in

predicting the weather? _____

_____

_____

_____

3. **Scientists at Work** Meteorologists must carefully **measure** conditions to **gather** and **record data** to put together maps that will help them **predict** the weather. How would the measurements from a weather satellite differ from those that you took? How would this be helpful to meteorologists?

_____

_____

_____

Investigate Further Try making a long-range weather forecast. After **recording data** on weather conditions from several station models, **predict** the weather for the next three days. Then write a summary report that includes data collected and

conclusions drawn from that data. _____

_____

_____

_____

Harcourt

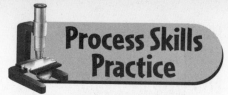

Measure to Gather Data

One way to gather data is by measuring and recording the conditions of an experiment or an event. To make measurements that are reproducible and useful for comparisons, it is often necessary to define the specific conditions under which the measurements are to be made.

Think About Measuring to Gather Data

The National Weather Service specifies that temperature readings be taken 5 feet above the ground, over shaded grass, in a ventilated box. To see if this is important, imagine the following experiment. The experiment is done on a sunny day. The temperature is measured and recorded 5 feet above the ground, over grass in a shaded area, and then over grass in the sun. Then the temperature is measured and recorded 5 feet above shaded asphalt and above asphalt that is in the sun.

1. Where would the temperature be the hottest? _____

   _____

2. Where would the temperature be the coolest? _____

3. Why do you think the National Weather Service has standard conditions for

   measuring air temperature? _____

   _____

   _____

4. Which thermometer will be closer to the actual air temperature: the thermometer over shaded grass or the thermometer over grass in the sun? Why?

   _____

   _____

   _____

   _____

5. Suppose that during the night there is a freezing rain. You check your thermometers in the morning and find them completely encased in ice. Which thermometer will show the highest temperature? Explain. _____

   _____

   _____

Harcourt

How Can Weather Be Predicted?

Lesson Concept

Meteorologists use data collected at weather stations to make surface maps. They can use the data and the maps to predict weather.

Vocabulary

forecast (B68)	**station model** (B68)	**surface map** (B68)
weather balloon (B69)	**weather map** (B70)	

Answer each question with one or more complete sentences.

1. Name five pieces of information you could find on a station model.

   _____

   _____

2. What is shown on a surface map? _____

   _____

3. Why are short-term weather forecasts more accurate than they used to be, but long-term forecasts still are not very accurate? _____

   _____

   _____

4. List three instruments you would expect to find at a weather station, and give their uses. _____

   _____

   _____

5. An air mass from the Gulf of Mexico is pushing north into Pittsburgh, which has been under the influence of a Canadian air mass for several days. What are the conditions now in Pittsburgh, and what will they be two or three days from now? _____

   _____

Harcourt

Local Weather Conditions

Materials

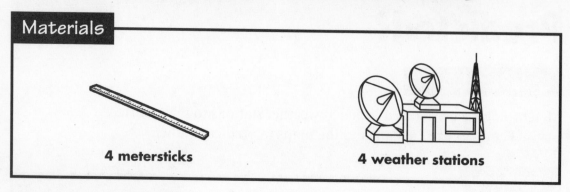

4 metersticks

4 weather stations

Activity Procedure

1. Use the table below.

Local Weather Conditions			
Location	Temperature	Wind Direction	Wind Speed
1			
2			
3			
4			

2. Choose four locations near your school to study. Select different kinds of locations, such as a shady parkway, a sunny playground, a parking lot on the south side of your school, and a ball field on the north side. For the same time on any given day, **predict** whether the temperature, wind direction, and wind speed will be the same or different at the different locations.

3. At the chosen time, four people should each take a meterstick and a weather station to a different one of the selected locations. Use the meterstick to locate a point 1 m above the ground. **Measure** and **record** the temperature at that point. Use the weather station to determine the wind direction and speed, too. Record the data in your table.

4. Make a double-bar graph to show the temperatures and wind speeds recorded at all the locations. Write the wind direction at each location on the appropriate wind-speed bar.

Harcourt

Name _____

Draw Conclusions

1. Use your table to **compare** the temperature, wind direction, and wind speed at the different locations. What differences, if any, did you find?

_____

_____

_____

_____

2. Local weather conditions affect the organisms that live in a location. Do you think wind speed or temperature is more likely to affect living organisms? Explain. _____

_____

_____

_____

3. Based on your investigation, how would you define the phrase *local weather conditions*? _____

_____

_____

4. **Scientists at Work** Scientists learn about local weather conditions by **comparing** weather data from different locations. **Draw conclusions** about local weather conditions, based on the locations you studied. What other information is needed to support your conclusions? _____

_____

_____

_____

Investigate Further What other factors, in addition to temperature, wind direction, and wind speed, might affect local weather conditions? **Hypothesize** about a factor that might affect local weather conditions. Then **plan and conduct a simple investigation** to test your hypothesis. Write instructions that others could follow in carrying out the procedure. _____

_____

_____

_____

Name _____

Date _____

Compare and Draw Conclusions

When you compare objects or events, you look for what they have in common. You also look for differences between them.

Think About Comparing and Drawing Conclusions

Earth's climates can be grouped into five major climate zones. In this activity you can compare three of those climate zones. Use the map and the descriptions of three world climates to answer the questions below.

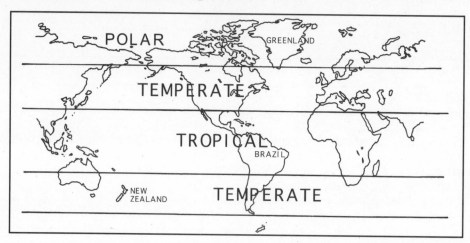

Polar climates are the world's coldest. Winter temperatures fall below −50°C.

Temperate climates have four seasons a year, with a warm or hot summer and a cool or dry winter. Average daily temperatures range between −3°C in the winter and 18°C in the summer. These areas have an average amount of precipitation.

Tropical climates are found in most of Earth's rain forests and savannas. These areas have an average daily temperature of 27°C and high rainfall.

1. Do you think the climate of Brazil is similar to or different from that of

   Greenland? Explain. _____

   _____

2. Do you think the climate in New Zealand would be very different from the

   climate in New Jersey? _____

   _____

   _____

Harcourt

What Is Climate and How Does It Change?

Lesson Concept

Climate is the average of all weather conditions through all seasons over a period of time. Earth's climate has changed over time as average temperatures have risen and fallen. Human activities can affect climate.

Vocabulary

climate (B76)   **microclimate** (B76)   **El Niño** (B79)

greenhouse effect (B80)   **global warming** (B80)

Fill in the chart with information from your textbook and answer the questions.

Climate Zones	Summer Temp.	Winter Temp.	Precipitation	Where Found?
Polar	cool	cold	snow	near North and South Poles
Mountain				
Temperate				
Tropical				

1. Which climate zones are coldest? _____

2. Which climate zone is wettest? _____

3. Which climate zone shows the most variation over a year? _____

4. How did putting information in a chart help you compare the climate zones?

_____

Harcourt

Vocabulary Review

Recognize Vocabulary

Underline the vocabulary term that best completes each sentence.

1. An arrangement of symbols and numbers that shows weather conditions at a weather station is a ____.

    A weather map   **B** surface map   **C** forecast   **D** station model

2. A ____ shows data about recent weather conditions across a large area.

    A station model   **B** weather map   **C** microclimate   **D** global warming

3. The average of all weather conditions through all seasons over a period of time is ____.

    A weather   **B** climate   **C** El Niño   **D** global warming

4. The ____ is caused by carbon dioxide in the atmosphere that absorbs heat given off by the Earth.

    A climate   **B** El Niño   **C** greenhouse effect   **D** microclimate

5. A ____ is a prediction of what the weather will be like in the future.

    A forecast   **B** station model   **C** surface map   **D** weather map

6. ____ is a short-term climate change that disrupts weather around the Pacific Ocean.

    A El Niño   **B** Global warming   **C** Microclimate   **D** The greenhouse effect

7. ____ is the climate of a very small area.

    A Global warming   **B** Microclimate   **C** Weather   **D** El Niño

8. A ____ shows station models and information about fronts and high and low pressure areas.

    A surface map   **B** forecast   **C** station model   **D** microclimate

Harcourt

Chapter 4 • Graphic Organizer for Chapter Concepts

Earth and the Moon

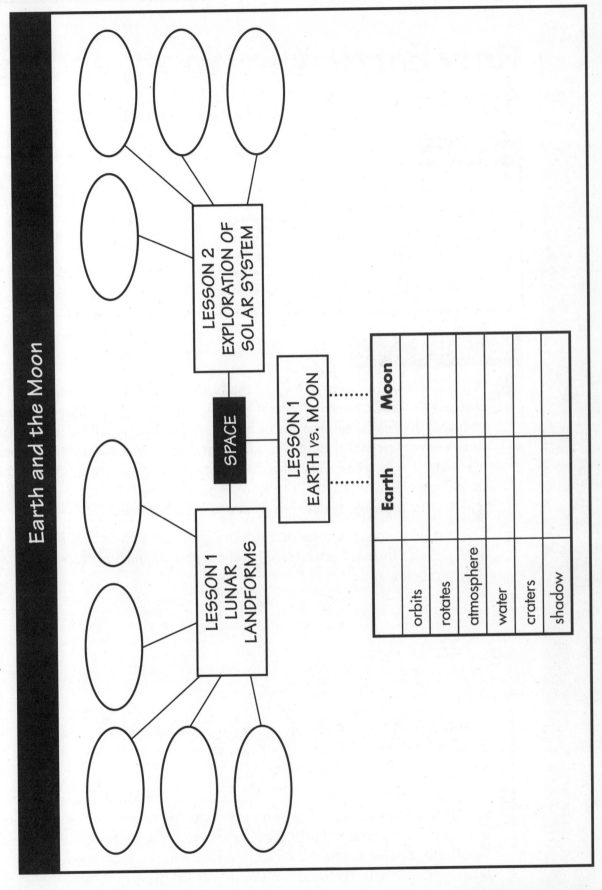

LESSON 2
EXPLORATION OF
SOLAR SYSTEM

SPACE

LESSON 1
EARTH vs. MOON

LESSON 1
LUNAR
LANDFORMS

	Earth	Moon
orbits		
rotates		
atmosphere		
water		
craters		
shadow		

Name _____

Date _____

How Earth, the Moon, and the Sun Move Through Space

Materials

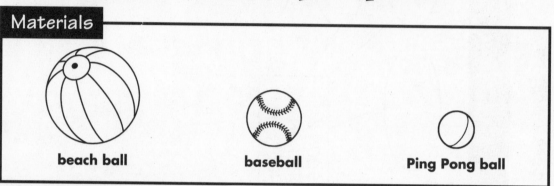

beach ball   baseball   Ping Pong ball

Activity Procedure

1 You will work in a group of four to **make a model** of the sun, Earth, and the moon in space. One person should stand in the center of a large open area and hold the beach ball over his or her head. The beach ball stands for the sun. A second person should stand far from the "sun" and hold the baseball overhead. The baseball stands for Earth. The third person should hold the Ping Pong ball near "Earth." The Ping Pong ball stands for the moon. The fourth person should **observe** and **record** what happens.

2 The real Earth moves around the sun in a path like a circle that has been pulled a little at both ends. This shape, called an *ellipse* (ee•LIPS), is shown below.

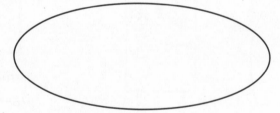

For the model, Earth should move around the sun in an ellipse-shaped path. Earth should also spin slowly as it moves around the sun. The observer should **record** this motion.

3 While Earth spins and moves around the sun, the moon should move around Earth in another ellipse-shaped path. The moon should also spin once as it moves around Earth. The same side of the moon should always face Earth. That is, the moon should spin once for each complete path it takes around Earth. The observer should **record** these motions.

Harcourt

Draw Conclusions

1. Your model shows three periods of time—a year, a month, and a day. Think about the time it takes Earth to spin once, the moon to move around Earth once, and Earth to move around the sun once. Which period of time does each

movement stand for? _____

_____

_____

_____

_____

2. Compare the movements of the moon to those of Earth.

_____

_____

_____

_____

_____

3. Scientists at Work Scientists often **make models** to show **time and space relationships** in the natural world. However, models can't always show these relationships exactly. How was your model of Earth, the moon, and the sun

limited in what it showed? _____

_____

_____

_____

Investigate Further Develop a testable question about the amount of sunlight that reaches Earth. Then **plan and conduct a simple investigation** to show how the amount of sunlight reaching Earth changes as Earth moves around the sun. Write instructions others can follow to carry out the procedure.

_____

_____

_____

_____

_____

Harcourt

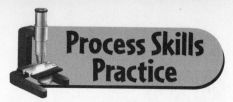

Use Time and Space Relationships

Time relationships tell you the order of events. Space relationships tell you about locations of objects. Understanding these relationships can help you make accurate models.

Think About Using Time and Space Relationships

Suppose you are a space traveler from Earth and you have just discovered a new solar system. You want to make an accurate map for those who will follow you. Answer these questions to plan your map. Use a separate sheet of paper if you need more space.

1. Think about mapping a new solar system. What space relationships will you show? _____

   _____

   _____

2. Seven large objects orbit a single star. Three of them have smaller objects orbiting them. What do the locations of the orbits tell you about the objects?

   _____

   _____

3. One of the seven larger orbiting objects is very close to the star. Three are a little farther away. Three are very far away. In which group are you most likely

   to find a planet to colonize? Explain. _____

   _____

4. Why is it important to show the locations of the planets accurately?

   _____

   _____

   _____

5. What would happen if you made a mistake in showing the locations of some of

   the planets or moons? _____

   _____

   _____

Harcourt

Concept Review

How Do Earth and the Moon Compare?

Lesson Concept

The moon revolves around Earth. The Earth-moon system revolves around the sun. Both Earth and the moon rotate on axes and have day-night cycles. Many features on Earth and the moon are different, but some landforms occur on both.

Vocabulary

revolve (B92)	**orbit** (B93)	**rotate** (B93)
axis (B93)	**eclipse** (B94)	

Select words from the box below to label the diagram. Watch out! Not every word in the box can be used to label the diagram, so you'll have to pick and choose.

lunar mare	gibbous	orbit	moon	full moon
day-night cycle	sun	Earth	eclipse	crater
quarter moon	half moon	axes	revolve	rotation

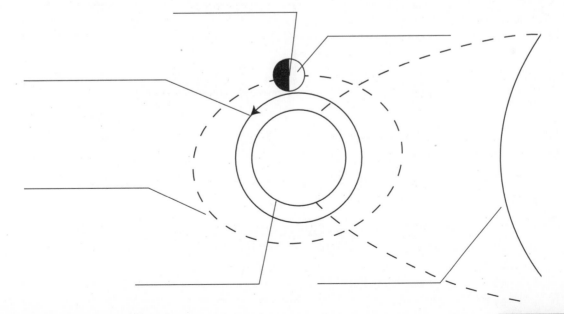

Harcourt

The Moon's Craters

Materials

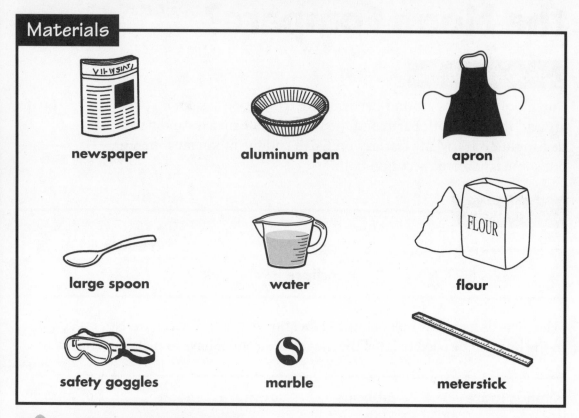

newspaper

aluminum pan

apron

large spoon

water

flour

safety goggles

marble

meterstick

CAUTION Activity Procedure

❶ Use the following table.

Trial	Height	Width of Craters
1	20 cm	
2	40 cm	
3	80 cm	
4	100 cm	

❷ Put the newspaper on the floor. Place the pan in the center of the newspaper.

❸ Use a large spoon to mix the water and flour in the aluminum pan. The look and feel of the mixture should be like thick cake batter. Now lightly cover the surface of the mixture with dry flour.

❹ **CAUTION** **Put on the safety goggles and apron** to protect your eyes and clothes from flour dust. Drop the marble into the pan from a height of 20 cm.

Harcourt

5 Carefully remove the marble and **measure** the width of the crater. **Record** the measurement in the table. Repeat Steps 4 and 5 two more times.

6 Now drop the marble three times each from heights of 40 cm, 80 cm, and 100 cm. Measure the craters and record the measurements after each drop.

Draw Conclusions

1. **Compare** the height from which each marble was dropped to the size of the crater it made. How does height affect crater size? _____

_____

_____

2. The Copernicus (koh•PER•nih•kuhs) crater on the moon is 91 km across. Based on your model, what can you **infer** about the object that formed this crater?

_____

_____

_____

3. **Scientists at Work** Most of the moon's craters were formed millions of years ago. Scientists **use models** to **infer** events that occurred too long ago to **observe** directly. What did you infer from the model about how the moon's craters formed? What other information do you need to draw conclusions about the

formation of the moon's craters? _____

_____

_____

_____

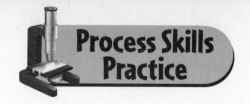

Infer

You infer when you use logical reasoning to draw conclusions based
on observations. An inference based on logical reasoning and
observation is always valid, even though it may not be correct.

Think About Inferring

Imagine you are in a spacecraft flying over the surface of an unexplored planet
that is about the same size as Earth. Crewless probes have reported that the planet
is composed of material that is common to both the moon and Earth. You are the
first human to see this planet. Looking down through thin, moving clouds, you
notice that there are craters and a lot of areas that look like the maria of the
moon. Most of the craters look worn and old, but a few have high, sharp sides and
look new. Some of the craters have steam rising from them and are surrounded by
a plain made of fresh material. Others are in rougher areas and are surrounded by
material that has been thrown out over the ground. You also notice very large
fields of what look like sand dunes.

1. From your observations of the new planet, what can you infer about how the

   craters were formed? Explain. _____

   _____

   _____

   _____

   _____

2. What can you infer about life on this planet? _____

   _____

   _____

   _____

   _____

3. What can you infer about weather on this planet? _____

   _____

   _____

   _____

   _____

Harcourt

Name _____

Date _____

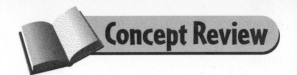

How Have People Explored Space?

Lesson Concept

People have studied objects in space since ancient times. They began by using their unaided eyes and then the telescope. Today they also use satellites and space probes. In the future, people may live and work on space stations and moon bases.

Vocabulary

telescope (B101)   **satellite** (B101)   **space probe** (B102)

Write the letter of an event next to the year it occurred.

_____ 900

_____ 1609

_____ 1668

_____ 1936

_____ 1957

_____ 1961

_____ 1969

_____ 1977

_____ 1981

A The Soviet Union launches *Sputnik 1*, the first artificial satellite.

B *Voyager I* and *Voyager II* space probes are launched. They have sent back pictures of Jupiter, Saturn, Uranus, and Neptune and are traveling beyond the solar system.

C The Mercury program sends the first Americans into space.

D Mayan people build an observatory for viewing the stars and planets at Chichén Itzá, in Mexico, around this date.

E Space shuttles began to be used to lift heavy cargoes into orbit; to provide labs for scientific research in space; and to launch, bring back, and repair satellites.

F Galileo uses a telescope to observe four moons orbiting Jupiter.

G American astronaut Neil Armstrong is the first person to walk on the moon.

H Sir Isaac Newton designs a telescope that uses a mirror as well as lenses to produce sharper images than those produced by Galileo's telescope.

I The first radio telescope is built and detects radio waves coming from objects in space.

Harcourt

Recognize Vocabulary

Read the following sentences. On each line, write the letter for the word or phrase that could be substituted for the vocabulary term in italics.

_____ 1. In 1609 Galileo used a *telescope* to observe craters on the moon.

  A artificial satellite
  B robot vehicle used to explore space
  C instrument that makes distant objects appear nearer

_____ 2. As it travels around the sun, Earth *rotates*.

  A spins on its axis
  B travels in a closed path
  C moves in an ellipse

_____ 3. The *Voyager space probes* have sent pictures of distant planets back to Earth.

  A artificial satellites
  B robot vehicles used to explore space
  C instruments that make distant objects appear nearer

_____ 4. Earth's *axis* travels through its North Pole and South Pole.

  A imaginary line that passes through Earth's center
  B elliptical path that Earth travels around the sun
  C shadow that Earth casts over the moon at some points in its orbit

_____ 5. Gravity makes the Earth-moon system *revolve* around the sun.

  A spin on its axis
  B travel in a closed path
  C face the sun as it moves

_____ 6. A total lunar *eclipse* lasts more than two hours and can be seen from any place on Earth that is facing the moon.

  A passage through Earth's shadow
  B trip around Earth in an elliptical path
  C volcanic eruption that leaves pools of dark lava on the moon

_____ 7. Earth's *orbit* around the sun is an ellipse, a shape that is nearly but not quite circular.

  A path as it revolves
  B imaginary line that passes through the center and the poles
  C shadow cast that causes an eclipse

Harcourt

Chapter 5 • Graphic Organizer for Chapter Concepts

The Solar System

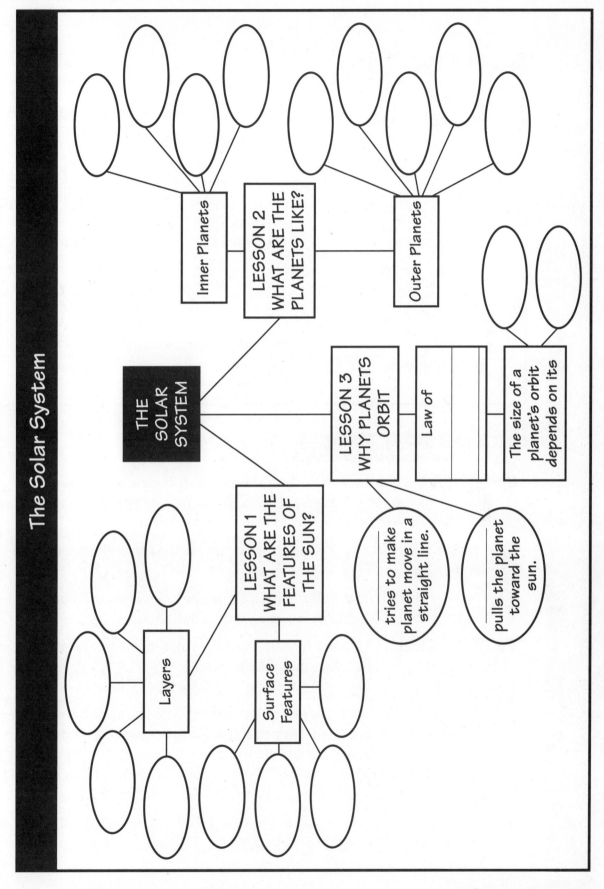

Sunspots

Materials

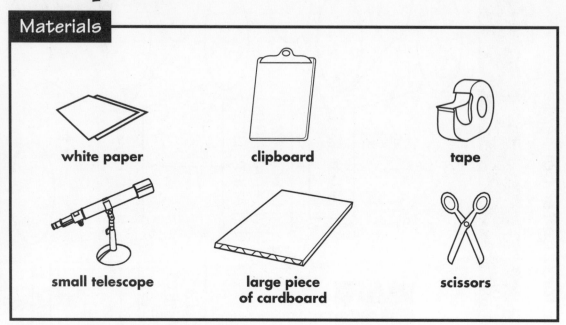

white paper

clipboard

tape

small telescope

large piece of cardboard

scissors

CAUTION ## Activity Procedure

1 **CAUTION** **Never look directly at the sun. You can cause permanent damage to your eyes.** Fasten the white paper to the clipboard. Tape the edges down to keep the wind from blowing them.

2 Center the eyepiece of the telescope on the cardboard, and trace around the eyepiece.

3 Cut out the circle, and fit the eyepiece into the hole. The cardboard will help block some of the light and make a shadow on the paper.

4 Point the telescope at the sun, and focus the sun's image on the white paper. **Observe** the image of the sun on the paper.

5 On the paper, outline the image of the sun. Shade in any dark spots you see. The dark spots are called *sunspots*. **Record** the date and time on the paper. **Predict** what you think will happen to the sunspots in the next day or two. *Note:* Since the image of the sun on the paper is reversed, any movement you **observe** will also be reversed. For example, movement from right to left on the image, represents movement from west to east on the sun.

6 Repeat Step 5 each sunny day for several days. **Record** the date, the time, and the positions of the sunspots each day.

Harcourt

Draw Conclusions

1. How did the positions of the sunspots change? _____

_____

_____

_____

_____

2. What can you **infer** from the movement of sunspots? _____

_____

_____

_____

_____

3. Scientists at Work Scientists **draw conclusions** from what they **observe**. Galileo was the first scientist to observe that it takes a sunspot about two weeks to cross from the left side of the sun's surface to the right side. Two weeks later, the sunspot appears on the left side of the sun's surface again. From this information, what conclusions can you draw about the time it takes the sun to make one complete rotation? What other information do you need to support your

conclusions? _____

_____

_____

_____

Investigate Further Does the sun always have the same number of spots? Do sunspots change in size? **Plan and conduct a simple investigation** to find answers to these and any other questions you might have about sunspots. Write

instructions others can follow to carry out the procedure. _____

_____

_____

_____

_____

_____

_____

_____

Harcourt

Name _____

Date _____

Process Skills
Practice

Draw Conclusions

Drawing conclusions involves the use of other process skills, such as
observing. Unlike inferences, conclusions are usually based on much
more data and should be tested repeatedly.

Think About Drawing Conclusions

In ancient times two astronomers were watching sunspots. The first astronomer
concluded the spots were planets orbiting the sun. The second astronomer
watched the sunspots more closely than the first. He noticed the spots changed
shape as they approached the edge of the sun's image. They became compressed
and then seemed to disappear. The second astronomer concluded the spots were
part of the sun's surface.

1. Why do you think the two astronomers came to such different conclusions?

_____

_____

2. What other data could the astronomers have gathered to support their

conclusions? _____

_____

_____

3. Astronomers over the ages have kept records of sunspots. The following is a
graph showing the appearance of sunspots from 1900 to 2001. What

conclusions can you draw from the graph? _____

_____

_____

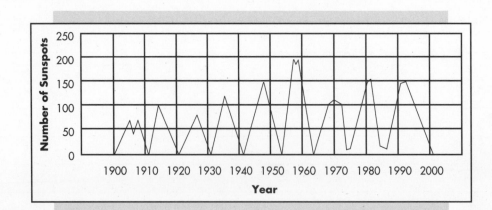

Harcourt

WB120 Workbook

Use with page B115.

Name _____

Date _____

Concept Review

What Are the Features of the Sun?

Lesson Concept

The sun is the source of almost all the energy on Earth. The sun has layers and visible surface features.

Vocabulary

photosphere (B119)	**corona** (B119)	**sunspot** (B120)
solar flare (B120)	**solar wind** (B120)	

Vocabulary terms and other words from this lesson are listed in the chart below. Choose the correct term for each blank attached to a part of this diagram of the sun.

corona	core	solar flare	convection zone
solar wind	photosphere	sunspot	radiation zone

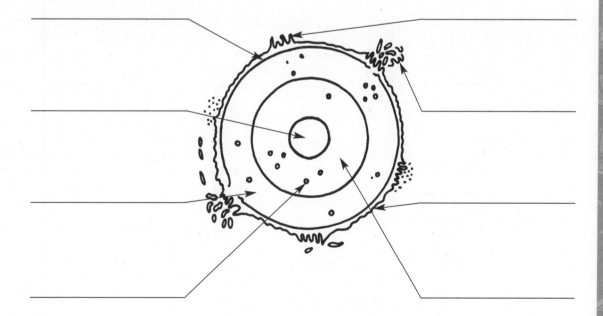

Harcourt

Name _____

Date _____

Investigate Log

Distances Between Planets

Materials

piece of string
about 4 m long

9 different-
colored markers

meterstick

Activity Procedure

1. Use the table below.

2. At one end of the string, tie three or four knots at the same point to make one large knot. This large knot will stand for the sun in your model.

Planet	Average Distance from the Sun (km)	Average Distance from the Sun (AU)	Scale Distance (cm)	Planet's Diameter (km)	Marker Color
Mercury	58 million	$\frac{4}{10}$	4	4876	
Venus	108 million	$\frac{7}{10}$	7	12,104	
Earth	150 million	1		12,756	
Mars	228 million	2		6794	
Jupiter	778 million	5		142,984	
Saturn	1429 million	10		120,536	
Uranus	2871 million	19		51,118	
Neptune	4500 million	30		49,532	
Pluto	5900 million	39		2274	

Harcourt

3 In the solar system, distances are often measured in astronomical units (AU). One AU equals the average distance from Earth to the sun. In your model, 1 AU will equal 10 cm. Use your meterstick to accurately measure 1 AU from the sun on your model. This point stands for Earth's distance from the sun. Use one of the markers to mark this point on the string. Note in your table which color you used.

4 Complete the Scale Distance column of the table. Then measure and mark the position of each planet on the string. Use a different color for each planet, and **record** in your table the colors you used.

Draw Conclusions

1. In your **model**, how far from the sun is Mercury? _____

How far away is Pluto? _____

2. What advantages can you think of for using AU to measure distances inside the solar system? _____

_____

_____

_____

_____

3. **Scientists at Work** Explain how it helped to **make a model** instead of

trying to show actual distances between planets. _____

_____

_____

_____

Investigate Further You can use a calculator to help make other scale models. The table gives the actual diameters of the planets. Use this scale: Earth's diameter = 1 cm. Find the scale diameters of the other planets by dividing their actual diameters by Earth's diameter. Make a scale drawing showing the diameter of each

planet. _____

_____

_____

_____

_____

Harcourt

Name _____

Date _____

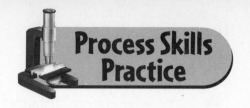

Make a Model

Making scale models can help you understand size relationships
among different objects.

Think About Making a Model

The table below lists the sizes of some of the different planets and their moons.

Object	Diameter	Object	Diameter
Jupiter	142,800 km	Earth	12,756 km
Ganymede	5270 km	Moon	3484 km
Europa	3275 km	Mars	6794 km
Amalthea	265 km	Deimos	15 km
		Phobos	27 km

1. Compare the diameter of Jupiter with the diameters of its moons. If you were
   going to make scale models less than 3 meters wide of Jupiter and these three
   moons, which scale would you choose? Circle your choice.

   A 10 km = 1 cm   **B** 100 km = 1 cm   **C** 1000 km = 1 cm

2. Tell how big each object would be using the scale you chose above.

   Jupiter _____   Europa _____

   Ganymede _____   Amalthea _____

3. Would it work to use the same scale you used for Jupiter for making models of

   Mars and its moons? Why or why not? _____

   _____

   _____

4. Pick a scale from Question 1 for making models of Earth and Earth's moon.
   Write down your scale and the size each of these objects would be.

   Scale _____

   Earth _____

   Moon _____

Harcourt

Name _____

Date _____

What Are the Planets Like?

Lesson Concept

Each planet in our solar system is unique.

Vocabulary

solar system (B124)   **planet** (B124)   **asteroids** (B127)   **comet** (B127)

Answer the questions about the planets.

1. What are three ways Mercury is like Earth's moon? _____

_____

_____

2. Compare and contrast Venus with Earth. _____

_____

_____

3. Give three facts about the geology of Mars. _____

_____

_____

4. How are Jupiter and Saturn alike and different? _____

_____

_____

_____

5. How are Uranus and Neptune alike and different? _____

_____

_____

_____

6. What causes a comet to form a long, glowing tail? _____

_____

_____

Harcourt

Use with page B129.

Workbook   WB125

Name _____

Date _____

Orbits

Materials

2-m string

safety goggles

metal washers

CAUTION

Activity Procedure

1 Tie three or four metal washers securely to one end of the string.

2 **CAUTION** **Take the string with the washers outside to an open area. Be sure that you are far from any buildings or objects and that no one is standing close to you. Put on the safety goggles.** Hold the loose end of the string. Slowly swing the string and washers in a circle above your head. **Observe** the motion of the washers.

3 **Predict** what will happen if you let go of the string while swinging it in a circle.

4 **CAUTION** **Again, make sure that there are no people, buildings, or other objects near you.** Swing the string and washers in a circle again. Let the string slip through your fingers. **Observe** the motion of the washers. How does it **compare** with your prediction?

5 Using a drawing, **record** the motion of the washers in Steps 2 and 4. Be sure to show the forces acting in each situation. Now make a drawing of the moon orbiting Earth. **Compare** the two drawings.

Harcourt

Name _____

Draw Conclusions

1. **Compare** the path of the washers while you were swinging them with their
   path once you let go of the string. _____

   _____

   _____

   _____

2. The string and washers can be used to **model** the moon orbiting Earth.
   Compare the motion of the washers circling your head with the motion
   of the moon orbiting Earth. _____

   _____

   _____

   _____

3. **Scientists at Work** When scientists **experiment**, they must **communicate** their
   results to others. One way of doing this is with diagrams. Look at the drawing
   you made of the washers. What motions and forces does it show?

   _____

   _____

   _____

   _____

Investigate Further Hypothesize about the effect the length of the string has on
the time the washers take to complete one revolution. Test your hypothesis. Then
write a report that includes tests conducted, data collected or evidence examined,
and conclusions drawn. _____

_____

_____

_____

Harcourt

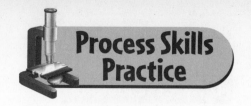

Communicate

When you communicate in science, you are showing the results of an activity, such as an experiment, in an organized fashion so that the results can be interpreted later. If you communicate well, you or someone else can repeat the experiment to demonstrate it to others, or you can build on the work to make further discoveries.

Think About Communicating

In the 1600s a mathematician named Johannes Kepler was given an assignment to analyze records of the motions of the planets to figure out the nature of their orbits. This was before telescopes, before Newton's laws of motion, and at a time when people knew very little about the planets. The records he studied had been kept very carefully by an astronomer named Tycho Brahe (TEE•koh BRAH•hee) and were considered very accurate. After studying the data, Kepler was able to describe the orbits of Mars and Earth as ellipses. He used this new information to figure out three laws of planetary motion, and he published his findings in two books. A few years afterward, a young scientist named Isaac Newton used the information communicated by Johannes Kepler to figure out the law of universal gravitation.

1. What kind of communication enabled Kepler to reach his conclusions?

   _____

2. How did Kepler communicate his own discoveries? _____

3. Kepler's books described the orbits of planets. If you were helping him write his books, how would you suggest he communicate his findings?

   _____

   _____

   _____

4. Part of effective scientific communication is making sure others will understand the information you are sharing. Do you think Brahe's scientific communication was effective? Was Kepler's? Explain. _____

   _____

   _____

   _____

Harcourt

Concept Review

Why Do the Planets Stay in Orbit?

Lesson Concept

The moon circles Earth in a path called an orbit. Gravitation between Earth and the moon keeps the moon from flying off into space because of its inertia. The balance between inertia and gravitation keeps Earth in orbit around the sun. It also keeps other planets and moons in their orbits.

Vocabulary

orbit (B132)   **law of universal gravitation** (B133)

Answer each question with one or more complete sentences.

1. If Earth suddenly disappeared, the moon would no longer be under its gravitational influence. Would the moon then fly off in a straight line? Explain. _____

    _____

2. Newton's law of universal gravitation says that all objects in the universe are attracted to all other objects. You already know this means that the moon is attracted toward Earth. Does the law of universal gravitation also mean that Earth is attracted toward the moon? Explain. _____

    _____

3. Gravitational force decreases with distance. What does this mean for a space traveler who leaves Earth in a spaceship? _____

    _____

    _____

4. As you travel through space away from Earth, what does the universal law of gravitation say about objects you may encounter that have huge masses ?

    _____

    _____

Harcourt

Recognize Vocabulary

Listed below are scrambled vocabulary terms from Chapter 5. Use the clues to unscramble the terms. Write each unscrambled term on the line provided.

1. BTIRO

   _____   path a body takes in space as it revolves around another body

2. FSLLAREARO

   _____   brief burst of energy from the sun's photosphere (2 words)

3. ONCORA

   _____   the sun's atmosphere

4. TDOIRAES

   _____   small, rocky object that orbits the sun in a belt between Mars and Jupiter

5. LPTANE

   _____   large object that moves around a star

6. HEPHRPOESOT

   _____   the sun's surface

7. VERINULASWALFOTIONARGVIAT

   _____   states that all objects in the universe are attracted to all other objects (4 words)

8. MOTEC

   _____   small mass of dust and ice that orbits the sun in a long, oval-shaped path

9. TPUNSOS

   _____   dark, cooler area of the sun's photosphere

10. MSTEYSRALOS

    _____   group of objects in space that move around a central star (2 words)

Harcourt

Name _____ Date _____

Chapter 1 • Graphic Organizer for Chapter Concepts

Matter and Its Properties

LESSON 1 PHYSICAL PROPERTIES	LESSON 2 CHANGES OF STATE	LESSON 3 CHEMICAL PROPERTIES
1. _____	1. _____	1. _____
2. _____	2. _____	2. _____
3. _____	3. _____	
4. _____	4. _____	
5. _____	5. _____	
	6. _____	

Using Physical Properties to Identify Objects

Materials

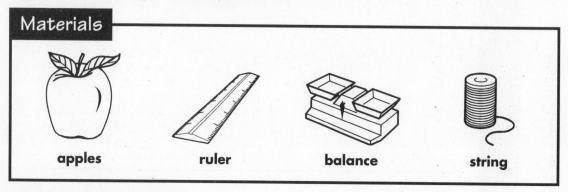

apples   ruler   balance   string

Activity Procedure

1 Carefully **observe** the apple your teacher gave you. What properties of your apple can you discover just by observing it? **Record** all the properties you observe.

2 Use the balance, ruler, and string to **measure** some characteristics of your apple. **Record** the properties you measure.

3 Put your apple in the pile of apples on your teacher's desk. Don't watch while your teacher mixes up the apples.

4 Using the properties that you recorded, try to identify your apple in the pile.

5 Using the balance, ruler, and string, **measure** this apple. **Compare** the measurements to those you recorded earlier. Then decide whether the apple you chose from the pile is yours. If someone else chose the same apple, comparing measurements should help you decide whose apple it really is.

Harcourt

Name _____

Draw Conclusions

1. **Compare** your apple with a classmate's apple. How are the two apples alike? How are they different? _____

_____

_____

2. Why was it helpful to **measure** some properties of your apple in addition to **observing** it? _____

_____

_____

3. How did you use the string to **measure** the apple? _____

_____

_____

4. **Scientists at Work** Scientists use both observations and measurements to identify substances. Which is faster, **observing** or **measuring**? Which provides more exact information? _____

_____

_____

Investigate Further Compare the list of your apple's properties with a classmate's list. Then, using both lists, come up with a way to **classify** an apple based on its physical properties. _____

_____

_____

_____

Harcourt

Observe and Measure

Observing is learning facts about something by using your senses.
Measuring, a form of observation, is learning facts by using
instruments that can be used to extend your senses.

Think About Observing and Measuring

Tanya's science teacher told the class that chemical elements do not break down
during normal laboratory reactions. Then she said that the iron in fortified cereal
is not an iron compound, but pure iron! To demonstrate, she poured the contents
of a box of iron-fortified cereal into a large bowl and crushed the cereal into a
powder. She mixed water into the powder until it was very thin
and watery. Then she took a small bar magnet taped to a
glass rod and stirred the cereal-and-water mixture
for several minutes. When she pulled the bar
magnet out, tiny bits of iron were clinging to it.

1. Tanya observed the iron clinging to the magnet. How could her class measure

   the amount of iron in the box of cereal? _____

   _____

   _____

2. Tanya and her classmates read on the side panel of the cereal box that one
   serving of the cereal met the recommended daily allowance for iron and that
   one cup of cereal was one serving. What observation and measurement could
   they do to see if the cereal really provided the recommended daily allowance

   for iron? _____

   _____

   _____

   _____

3. How did the iron become separated from the cereal? Did the chemical elements
   of the cereal break down when Tanya's teacher mixed it with water? Explain.

   _____

   _____

   _____

Harcourt

Name _____

Date _____

Concept Review

How Can Physical Properties Be Used to Identify Matter?

Lesson Concept

Matter has mass and takes up space. Physical properties can be used to identify different types of substances. Some physical properties, such as mass, volume, and density, can be measured.

Vocabulary

matter (C6) **physical properties** (C6) **mass** (C7) **weight** (C7)

volume (C8) **density** (C9) **solubility** (C10)

Choose the answer that best completes the statement.

1. The effect of gravity on matter is the measure of _____.

  A mass **B** weight **C** density

2. An object has a mass of 120 g on Earth. On the moon it would have a mass of _____.

  A 20 g **B** 60 g **C** 120 g

3. The density of a steel hammer is 7.9 g/cm^3 on Earth. On a spaceship it would have a density of _____.

  A 0 g/cm^3 **B** 3.9 g/cm^3 **C** 7.9 g/cm^3.

4. Matter is anything that has mass and _____.

  A occupies space **B** properties **C** size

Decide whether the underlined term makes each statement true or false. If the statement is true, write the word *true* on the line. If the statement is false, write a word or phrase that makes the statement true.

_____ **5.** Materials <u>are</u> changed when physical properties are measured.

_____ **6.** A milliliter is a unit of <u>volume</u>.

_____ **7.** In a <u>mixture</u>, the particles are evenly mixed.

Name _____

Date _____

Investigate Log

Changing States of Matter

Materials

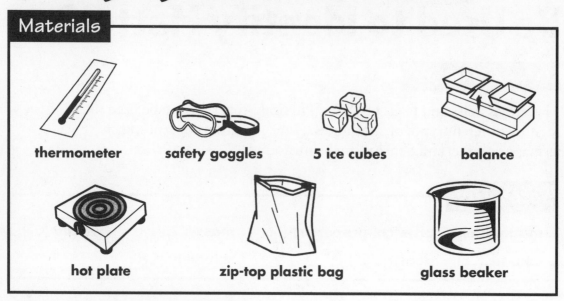

thermometer   safety goggles   5 ice cubes   balance

hot plate   zip-top plastic bag   glass beaker

CAUTION

Activity Procedure

1 Place five ice cubes in a zip-top plastic bag. Be sure to seal the bag. Use the balance to **measure** the mass of the ice cubes and the bag. **Observe** the shape of the ice cubes. **Record** your observations and measurements.

2 Set the bag of ice cubes in a warm place. **Observe** what happens to the shape of the ice cubes. **Measure** the mass of the melted ice cubes and the bag. Unzip the bag slightly and insert the thermometer. Measure the temperature of the water. **Record** your observations and measurements. Use your observations to **infer** that a change of state is occurring.

3 After the ice has completely melted, pour the water into a glass beaker. **Observe** what happens to the water's shape, and **record** the water's temperature.

4 **CAUTION** **Put on the safety goggles.** Your teacher will use a hot plate to heat the water in the beaker until it boils. **Observe** what happens to the water when it boils. **Record** the temperature of the boiling water. Use your observations to **infer** that a change of state has occurred.

Harcourt

Name _____

WB137

Draw Conclusions

1. Identify the different states of water at different points in this investigation.

_____

_____

_____

_____

2. **Compare** the mass of the ice to the mass of water after it melted. What does this show about changes in state? _____

_____

_____

3. What temperatures did you **record** as the water changed states? Make a table or a graph of your data. _____

_____

_____

4. **Scientists at Work** After scientists use their senses to **observe** the properties of substances, they can **infer** whether a change in state has taken place. What did you observe in this investigation? What did you infer about a change of state for each observation? _____

_____

_____

Investigate Further The physical change that happens to water when it is boiled produces water vapor—an invisible gas. Develop a testable question, or a hypothesis, about the relationship between the mass of the water vapor and the mass of the liquid water. _____

_____

_____

_____

_____

Harcourt

Name _____

Date _____

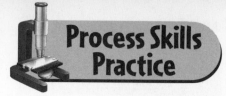

Observe and Infer

Observation is collecting information about something by using your
senses. Inferences are assumptions you make after considering your
observations. Observations are facts, but inferences are guesses and
may not always be correct.

Think About Observing and Inferring

Every night Dan could hear strange creaking noises in
his bedroom and from the hallway outside his door. He
finally asked his father about the noises and if the house
was haunted. "That's just the house," explained his father.
When Dan seemed doubtful, his father reached into the
recycle bin and found a long-necked bottle. "After the
sun goes down," he explained to Dan, "the house cools
and contracts, that is, it actually gets smaller." To
demonstrate, he partially inflated a balloon and put it
over the bottle's neck as shown in the drawing. When he
put the bottle into a bowl of ice water, the balloon
shrank and fell over. When he put the bottle outside in
the sun, the balloon slowly became inflated again.

1. What was Dan's first inference when he observed the noises in his house? Was

   his observation a fact? Was his inference correct? _____

   _____

2. What did he observe about the balloon and the bottle? _____

   _____

   _____

3. Why would Dan's house make noise expanding and contracting although the

   balloon did not? _____

   _____

   _____

Harcourt

How Does Matter Change from One State to Another?

Lesson Concept

Three states of matter are solid, liquid, and gas. Changes in state are physical changes. Particles of matter move faster as heat is added and slow down as heat is removed. Every substance has a melting point, the temperature at which it changes from a solid to a liquid. It also has a boiling point, the temperature at which it changes from a liquid to a gas.

Vocabulary

solid (C14)	**liquid** (C14)	**gas** (C14)
evaporation (C16)	**condensation** (C17)	

Identify the following characteristics as belonging to solids (S), liquids (L), or gases (G). Some characteristics belong to more than one state of matter.

_____ **1.** particles are held rigidly in place

_____ **2.** takes the shape of the container

_____ **3.** has a definite shape

_____ **4.** particles are touching

_____ **5.** particles slide over one another

_____ **6.** particles are far apart

Choose the answer that best completes the statement.

7. The freezing point of a substance is the same as its _____ point.

    A melting   **B** boiling   **C** condensation

8. Evaporation changes a _____.

    A gas to a liquid   **B** liquid to a solid   **C** liquid to a gas

9. When a substance freezes, it _____.

    A gains energy   **B** loses energy   **C** stays the same

10. Boiling involves the same change of state as _____.

    A freezing   **B** condensation   **C** evaporation

Harcourt

Chemical Properties

Materials

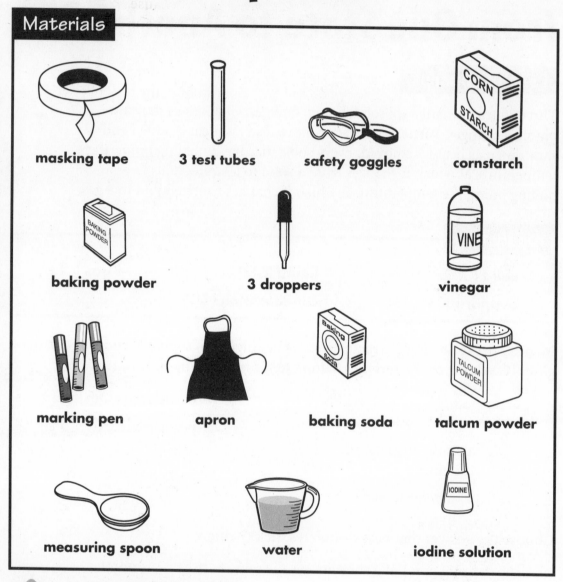

masking tape   3 test tubes   safety goggles   cornstarch

baking powder   3 droppers   vinegar

marking pen   apron   baking soda   talcum powder

measuring spoon   water   iodine solution

 CAUTION   Activity Procedure

1. Use the masking tape and marking pen to label your test tubes *water*, *vinegar*, and *iodine*.

2. **CAUTION** Put on the apron and safety goggles. Leave them on for the entire activity.

3. Put about $\frac{1}{3}$ spoonful of baking soda in each test tube. Add a dropper of water to the test tube labeled *water*. **Observe** and **record** what happens.

Harcourt

4 Add a dropper of vinegar to the test tube labeled *vinegar*. **Observe** and **record** what happens this time.

5 Add a dropper of iodine solution to the test tube labeled *iodine*. **CAUTION** Iodine is poisonous if swallowed and can cause stains. Be careful not to spill or touch the iodine solution. Wash your hands if you get iodine on them. **Observe** and **record** what happens.

6 Wash the test tubes with soap and water. Repeat Steps 3–5 three more times using cornstarch, talcum powder, and baking powder in the test tubes instead of baking soda. Be sure to wash the test tubes between tests. **Observe** and **record** what happens each time.

7 Get an "unknown" sample from your teacher. It will be one of the substances you have already tested. Test it with water, vinegar, and iodine solution, just as you did before. **Observe** and **record** what happens when you add each of the liquids. What is your unknown substance?

Draw Conclusions

1. Vinegar is one of a group of substances called *acids*. Acids react with substances called *bases*. Of the substances you tested, which are bases? How can you tell?

_____

2. Baking powder is not a pure substance. It is a mixture of two of the other substances you tested. Based on your results, what do you **infer** are the two

   substances in baking powder? _____

3. **Scientists at Work** Scientists **experiment** to find out if substances react. What signs of reactions (dependent variables) did you identify? What **variables** did you **control**? What was the independent variable (the one you changed) in each experiment? What did you learn as you changed this variable?

_____

_____

_____

_____

Investigate Further Suppose you wanted to discover some of the chemical properties of chalk. First develop a testable question. Then **experiment** to answer

your question. _____

_____

_____

_____

Harcourt

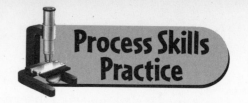

Experiment

One of the most basic of all activities in science is experimenting. Scientists state hypotheses and then design experiments to test them. Scientists change certain conditions in experiments and observe what happens. From these observations, they can see whether their hypotheses were correct.

Think About Experimenting

Sandra learned in science class that each substance has its own characteristic properties. One of those properties is density. Her teacher also said that the properties of a substance do not change even if the sample size changes. Sandra found that hard to believe. Sandra knew she could measure the density of a substance by putting it in water. If something floats, it is less dense than water. If it sinks, it is more dense than water. Sandra put some water in a clear jar and dropped in a piece of potato. The potato floated. Sandra hypothesized that a large enough piece of potato would sink. She put a large potato in the water and it also floated.

1. What was Sandra's hypothesis? _____

_____

_____

2. What did Sandra observe? Was her hypothesis supported by her experiment?

Why or why not? _____

_____

_____

_____

3. If the potato floats, then it is less dense than the water. Hypothesize what would happen if you could somehow make the water less dense.

_____

_____

4. Design an experiment that would test your hypothesis. _____

_____

_____

_____

_____

Harcourt

Name _____

Date _____

How Does Matter React Chemically?

Lesson Concept

Physical changes do not result in the formation of new substances. However, new substances are formed during chemical changes. Physical and chemical properties can be used to identify substances and to separate mixtures. Matter is neither produced nor destroyed during physical and chemical reactions.

Vocabulary

reactivity (C23)   **combustibility** (C24)

Answer each question with one or more complete sentences.

1. What is the difference between a physical change and a chemical change?

_____

_____

2. If you had a mixture of two substances and had your choice of using a physical change or a chemical change to separate them, which would you prefer?

Explain. _____

_____

_____

3. What is the relationship between the chemical properties of a substance and

the chemical changes of a substance? _____

_____

Identify each of the following as a physical or chemical change by writing
physical **or** *chemical* **on the line.**

4. a snow bank shrinking on a cold day   _____

5. forming a bar of gold into wire   _____

6. bleaching a sheet and pillowcase   _____

Harcourt

Recognize Vocabulary

Match the term on the left with its description on the right by
writing the letter of the description in the blank next to the term.

_____ 1. matter

_____ 2. solid

_____ 3. liquid

_____ 4. physical
    properties

_____ 5. gas

_____ 6. mass

_____ 7. evaporation

_____ 8. weight

_____ 9. condensation

_____ 10. volume

_____ 11. reactivity

_____ 12. density

_____ 13. combustibility

_____ 14. solubility

A the state of matter that has no definite shape
   or volume

B the pull of gravity on matter

C changing from a gas to a liquid

D the amount of matter in an object

E the ability of a substance to dissolve

F the changing of a liquid to a gas

G the ability of a substance to react chemically

H the characteristics of a substance that can be
   measured without changing the substance

I mass per unit of volume

J the state of matter with a definite shape
   and volume

K the ability to burn

L anything that has mass and occupies space

M the amount of space anything occupies

N the state of matter with a definite volume but
   no definite shape

Harcourt

Chapter 2 • Graphic Organizer for Chapter Concepts

Atoms and Elements

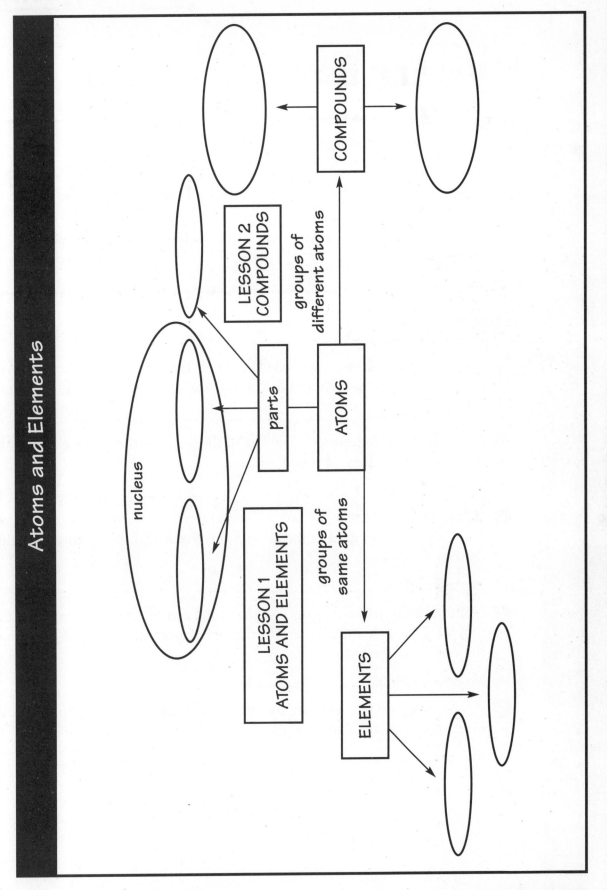

Name _____

Date _____

Mystery Boxes

Materials

sealed box
provided by
your teacher

ruler

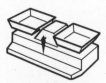
balance

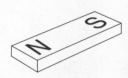
magnet

Activity Procedure

1 With a partner, **observe** the sealed box your teacher gave you. **Record** any observations you think might help you learn about what's inside the box.

My observations: _____

2 Use the ruler to **measure** the outside of the box. Use the balance to find the mass of the box. **Record** your results.

My measurements: _____

3 Carefully tilt and shake the box. How many objects do you **infer** are in the box? How big do you infer the objects are? **Record** your inferences and the reasons for them.

My inferences: _____

4 Hold the magnet to the surface of the box. Then tilt the box. Are any of the objects in the box attracted to the magnet? Repeat this at several places on the surface of the box.

My observations: _____

5 What objects do you **infer** are inside the box? Base your inferences on your measurements and observations.

My inferences: _____

Name _____

Investigate Log

6 What do you **infer** about the inside of the box? Draw a picture of what you think the inside of the box looks like.

7 Now open the box. **Compare** your inferences about the objects in the box with the objects the box really contains. Also compare your inferences about what the box looks like inside with what it really looks like.

My comparisons: _____

_____

_____

Draw Conclusions

1. How did what you **inferred** about the objects inside the box **compare** with what was really inside? _____

_____

2. How did what you **inferred** about the inside of the box **compare** with the way it really looked inside? _____

_____

3. Scientists at Work Different scientists may **infer** different things about objects they can't **observe** directly. Compare your inferences about the contents and the inside of the box with the inferences of other pairs. _____

_____

Investigate Further Construct your own mystery box, and place various objects inside it. Exchange boxes with a classmate. **Observe** the box and **draw conclusions** about its contents based on your observations. Indicate whether additional information is needed to support your conclusions.

_____

_____

_____

Harcourt

Name _____

Date _____

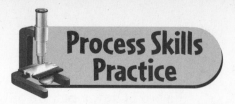

Observe and Infer

When you observe, you use one or more of your senses to perceive properties of objects and events. Observations can be made directly with the senses or indirectly through the use of instruments. When you infer, you use logical reasoning to draw conclusions based on observations. Inferences are explanations based on judgments and are not always correct.

Think About Observing and Inferring

During the investigation activity, you observed and inferred the characteristics of a mystery box. Below are some of the things you did during the investigation. After each action, write an *O* if you were observing or an *I* if you were inferring when you performed that step.

1. recorded things you noticed about the box	
2. used a ruler to measure the outside of the box	
3. listened to the sounds made and noticed the shifts in weight within the box when you tilted it and shook it	
4. drew a picture of what you thought the inside of the box looked like before you opened the box	

5. How did observing help you make an inference about the box?

_____

_____

_____

6. Suppose you receive a large envelope in the mail. Before opening it, you observe it and infer what is in it. What might you observe about the envelope?

_____

_____

_____

7. What are some things you could infer about an unopened letter?

_____

_____

Harcourt

What Are Atoms and Elements?

Lesson Concept

Atoms are tiny particles of matter. Elements are substances made up of only one kind of atom.

Vocabulary

nucleus (C41)	**proton** (C41)	**neutron** (C41)	**electron** (C41)
element (C42)	**atom** (C42)	**molecule** (C42)	

Below is a list of terms and names from this lesson. Put each term or name into the correct category by writing it under one of the headings below.

heat conductor	ductile	sodium	electron
iron	oxygen	Dalton	neutron
silicon	proton	malleable	Bohr
electrical conductor			

Subatomic Particles	Common Elements	Properties of Metals	Scientists Who Studied Atoms

Draw a picture of Bohr's model of an atom, and label each part.

Harcourt

Grouping Elements

Materials

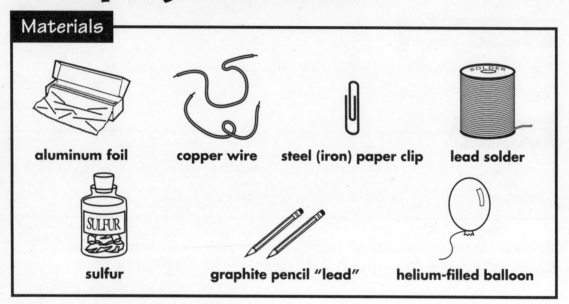

aluminum foil   **copper wire**   **steel (iron) paper clip**   **lead solder**

sulfur   **graphite pencil "lead"**   **helium-filled balloon**

CAUTION   ## Activity Procedure

1 Use the chart below to **record** the properties of the elements you **observe**.

Object	Element	Phase	Color	Luster	Malleability
foil					
wire					
paper clip					
sulfur					
graphite					
solder					
balloon					

2 What elements do the objects represent? **Record** your answers in the second column of the chart.

3 **Observe** each element. Is it a solid, a liquid, or a gas at room temperature? **Record** your observations in the column of the chart labeled "Phase."

Harcourt

Name _____

4 What is the color of each element? (Carefully release some of the helium from the balloon.) **Record** what you **observe** in the chart.

5 Which elements have luster? (Which are shiny?) **Record** what you **observe** in the fifth column of the chart.

6 Which elements bend easily? **Record** what you **observe** in the column labeled "Malleability." **CAUTION** **Wash your hands after handling the objects in this investigation.**

Draw Conclusions

1. What similar properties did you **observe** in different elements?

_____

_____

_____

2. Consider the properties you **observed.** Which elements do you **infer** could be

grouped together? Explain. _____

_____

3. **Scientists at Work** Scientists have made a periodic table, in which elements are classified, or grouped, by their properties. Using your observations, **predict** which elements from the activity are near each other in the periodic table.

_____

_____

Investigate Further Think of other properties that could be used to classify elements. **Plan and conduct a simple investigation** of some properties that would help you classify elements. Write instructions that others can follow to carry out

the procedure. _____

_____

_____

_____

Harcourt

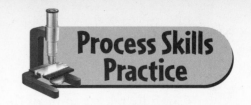

Predict

You can use observations to predict the outcomes of future events.
Before making scientific predictions, you should think about previous
observations you made of related events.

Think About Predicting

Observe the table below. Each element in the table is shown with its
atomic number and atomic mass. The atomic mass is the mass in
grams of one mole (6.02×10^{23} atoms) of an element.

Element	Atomic Number	Atomic Mass
Helium	2	4
Carbon	6	12
Nitrogen	7	14
Oxygen	8	16
Sodium	11	
Iron		56

1. How many electrons circle around the nucleus of each atom of oxygen? _____

2. Describe the relationship between atomic number and atomic mass in

   the table. _____

3. The atomic mass of sodium is missing. What would you predict the atomic

   mass to be? _____

4. The atomic number of iron is missing. What would you predict the atomic

   number to be? _____

5. The atomic mass of sodium is actually 23 g. The atomic number of iron is
   actually 26. Compare these values to your predictions in Questions 3 and 4.
   What does this tell you about the relationship you saw between atomic

   number and atomic mass? _____

   _____

   _____

Harcourt

What Are Compounds?

Lesson Concept

Compounds are molecules made of two or more elements.

Vocabulary

periodic table (C49)	**compound** (C50)

Chemists use shorthand to describe compounds. Use the table below to match each chemical symbol with the element it stands for.

C = carbon	Ca = calcium	Cl = chlorine	H = hydrogen
He = helium	O = oxygen	N = nitrogen	Na = sodium
Fe = iron			

1. One molecule of table salt (NaCl) has _____ atom(s) of

   _____ and _____ atom(s) of _____.

2. One molecule of water (H_2O) has _____ atom(s) of _____

   and _____ atom(s) of _____.

3. One molecule of methane (CH_4) has _____ atom(s) of

   _____ and _____ atom(s) of _____.

4. One molecule of ammonia (NH_3) has _____ atom(s) of

   _____ and _____ atom(s) of _____.

Circle the choice that best completes each sentence below.

5. The order of elements in the periodic table is based on the
   number of protons in one atom / *atomic mass*.

6. Elements with properties of metals and nonmetals are called
   metalloids / *semi-metals*.

7. A Russian chemist named Dmitri Mendeleev organized elements by
   atomic number / *atomic mass*.

Name _____

Date _____

Recognize Vocabulary

On the line, write the letter of the answer that best completes each sentence.

1. The _____ is the center of an atom.

   A nucleus   **B** proton   **C** compound   **D** molecule

2. A(n) _____ is made up of only one kind of atom.

   A compound   **B** element   **C** molecule   **D** atomic number

3. A(n) _____ is a subatomic particle with a negative charge.

   A electron   **B** nucleus   **C** neutron   **D** proton

4. The smallest unit of an element that has all the properties of that element is a(n) _____.

   A substance   **B** compound   **C** atom   **D** molecule

5. The elements are arranged in order of atomic number in the _____ table.

   A atomic   **B** Mendeleev   **C** periodic   **D** atomic mass

6. A(n) _____ is made of atoms of two or more elements.

   A neutron   **B** compound   **C** element   **D** molecule

7. A(n) _____ is a subatomic particle with a positive charge.

   A electron   **B** nucleus   **C** neutron   **D** proton

8. When two or more atoms are linked together, they form a(n) _____.

   A substance   **B** compound   **C** atom   **D** molecule

9. A(n) _____ is a subatomic particle with no charge.

   A electron   **B** nucleus   **C** neutron   **D** proton

Harcourt

Name _____ Date _____

Chapter 3 • Graphic Organizer for Chapter Concepts

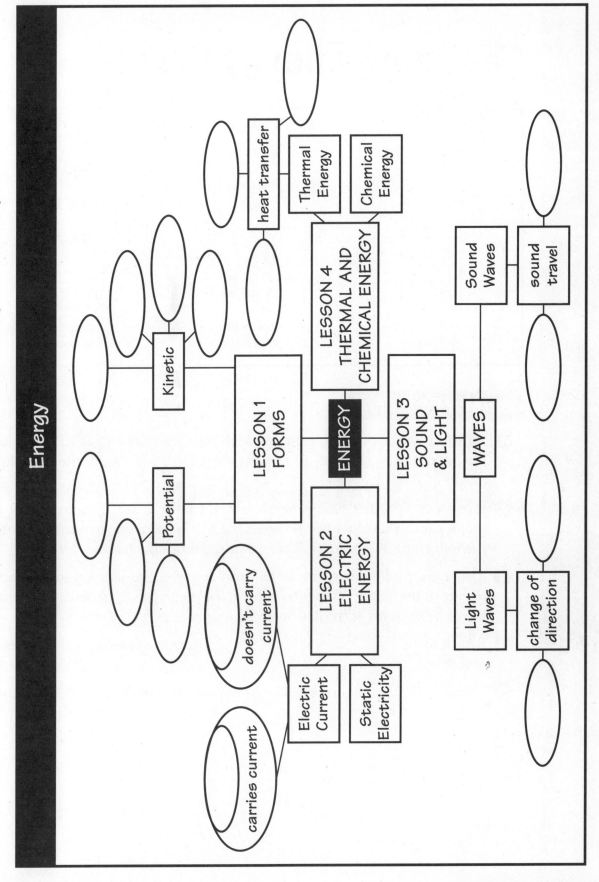

Name _____

Date _____

Changing Energy Forms

Materials

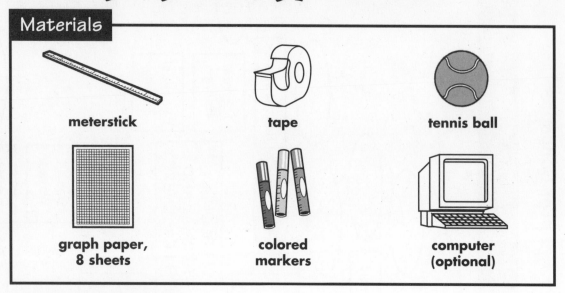

meterstick   tape   tennis ball

graph paper,   colored   computer
8 sheets   markers   (optional)

Activity Procedure

1 Tape four sheets of graph paper vertically to a wall. Starting at the floor, use the meterstick to mark off 10-cm intervals on the left edge of the paper to a height of 100 cm.

2 Work with a partner. One person sits on the floor about 0.5 m from the graph paper. The other person holds the tennis ball a few centimeters from the wall at the 50-cm mark. Then he or she drops the ball.

3 The seated person **observes** the ball as it bounces, and uses a colored marker to **record** the height of each bounce on the graph paper. **Count** and record the number of times the ball bounces.

4 Repeat Steps 2 and 3 several times. Use a different-colored marker to **record** each trial.

5 Replace the paper and repeat Steps 1–4, but this time drop the ball from a height of 100 cm.

Harcourt

Name _____

Draw Conclusions

1. **Compare** the drop height to the bounce height for each trial in the experiment. How are the heights related? _____

   _____

   _____

2. When you hold the ball in the air before dropping it, it has *potential energy* because of its position and because of gravitation. When you let go of the ball, it has *kinetic energy* because of its movement. **Infer** the point at which the ball has the most kinetic energy. _____

   _____

   _____

3. **Draw a conclusion** about how potential energy and kinetic energy are related in the bouncing ball. _____

   _____

   _____

4. **Scientists at Work** Scientists often use computers to help them **interpret data** and **communicate** the results of an experiment. Use a computer to write a report of your investigation. Be sure to describe the tests you conducted, and summarize your conclusions. _____

   _____

   _____

   _____

Investigate Further Analyze the data you collected and **predict** how high and how many times a ball dropped from a height of 200 cm will bounce. Then **experiment** and **compare** your results to your predictions. _____

_____

_____

_____

_____

Harcourt

Name _____

Date _____

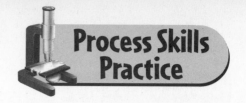

Communicate

When you communicate, you transmit data or information to others. You can use spoken or written words, graphs, drawings, diagrams, maps, and charts to communicate. Communicating in science means showing the results of an activity in an organized fashion so that the data can be interpreted or the activity repeated.

Think About Communicating

Here is some data from an experiment to observe the potential and kinetic energy of a basketball.

Dropped from 1 meter. Trial 1: Bounced 60 cm. Trial 2: Bounced 70 cm. Trial 3: Bounced 80 cm.

Dropped from 2 meters. Trial 1: Bounced 1 m 40 cm. Trial 2: Bounced 1 m 25 cm. Trial 3: Bounced 1 m 40 cm.

Communicate these results on the graphs.

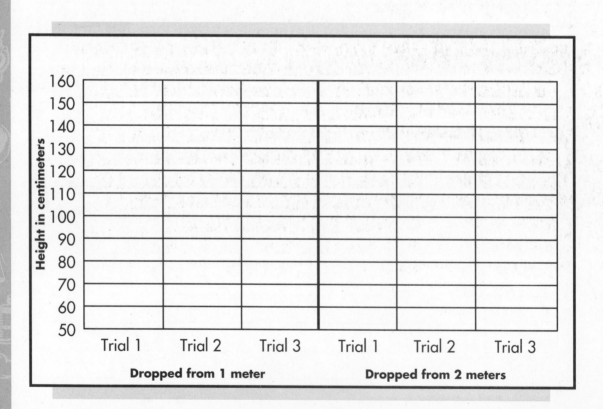

Harcourt

Concept Review

What Are Kinetic and Potential Energy?

Lesson Concept

Energy is the ability to cause changes in matter. There are two basic types of energy—kinetic energy and potential energy. Kinetic and potential energy can be found in many forms. Electric energy, thermal energy, mechanical energy, light, and sound are all forms of kinetic energy. Chemical potential energy, gravitational potential energy, and elastic potential energy are forms of potential energy. The law of conservation of energy says energy can change form but cannot be created or destroyed.

Vocabulary

energy (C64)	kinetic energy (C64)	potential energy (C64)

Decide whether the underlined term or phrase makes each statement true or false. If the statement is true, write the word *true* on the line. If the statement is false, write a word or phrase that makes the statement true.

_____ **1.** Energy is the <u>ability to do work</u>.

_____ **2.** The energy of motion is called <u>kinetic energy</u>.

_____ **3.** The energy an object has because of where it is or because of its condition is called <u>potential energy</u>.

_____ **4.** A boulder rolling down a hill has <u>potential</u> energy.

_____ **5.** Mechanical energy is a form of <u>potential</u> energy.

_____ **6.** Energy <u>never changes</u> from one form to another during any one activity.

_____ **7.** Thermal energy and light energy are two forms of <u>potential</u> energy.

_____ **8.** An apple that is ready to drop from the tree to the ground has gravitational <u>potential</u> energy.

_____ **9.** The energy stored in a compressed spring is called elastic <u>kinetic</u> energy.

Harcourt

Electric Circuits

Materials

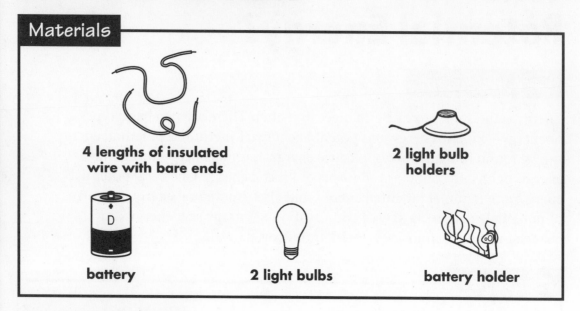

4 lengths of insulated wire with bare ends

2 light bulb holders

battery

2 light bulbs

battery holder

Activity Procedure

1. To make electricity flow between the terminals, or charged ends, of a dry cell or battery, you need to connect the terminals in some way, such as with a wire. Electricity will then flow through any device you put along this path. Connect the wires, bulb holders, and battery holder as shown in Picture A on page C69.

2. Insert the light bulbs and batteries. **Observe** what happens and **record** your observations.

3. Remove one of the bulbs from its holder. **Observe** and **record** what happens to the other bulb.

4. Now reconnect the wires, bulb holders, and battery holder as shown in Picture B on page C69. **Observe** what happens and **record** your observations.

5. Again remove one of the bulbs from its holder. **Observe** and **record** what happens to the other bulb.

6. Draw diagrams of both of the circuits you built. Use arrows to **compare** the path of the electric current in each circuit.

Harcourt

Name _____

 **Investigate Log**

Draw Conclusions

1. What happened to the other bulb when one bulb was removed from the first circuit? _____

2. What happened to the other bulb when one bulb was removed from the second circuit? _____

3. **Scientists at Work** Scientists often **compare** results before they **draw a conclusion**. Cross out one bulb in each of your drawings. Then diagram the path the electric current must take if it can't pass through the bulb you crossed out. Compare your diagrams, and then draw a conclusion about which type of circuit would be better to use for a string of lights. _____

_____

_____

_____

_____

Investigate Further In the investigation you demonstrated that electricity flowing through a circuit produces light and heat (the glowing bulbs were warm). Now **plan and conduct a simple investigation** to answer any questions you have about other effects that electricity flowing through a circuit can produce. Select the equipment you will need to use and decide what data you will need to collect.

_____

_____

_____

_____

Harcourt

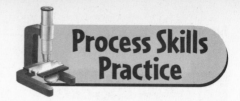

Compare and Draw Conclusions

When you compare, you identify common and distinguishing characteristics of objects or events. When you draw a conclusion, you pull together all that you have discovered in observing, researching, and investigating.

Think About Comparing and Drawing Conclusions

Comparing the characteristics of different things is a good way to learn those characteristics and draw conclusions about them. Look at the data in the chart below and then answer the questions that follow.

	Materials That Allow Electricity to Flow	Materials That Do Not Allow Electricity to Flow
Porous	watery substances, salt solutions, acid solutions	Leather, cotton, wool, parchment, ashes, chalk, hair, feathers, wood
Nonporous	iron, copper, silver, graphite, charcoal	rubber, porcelain, vinyl, plastics, precious stones, ceramic, glass, resin, amber

1. When you plug something into an electrical outlet, you don't want electricity to flow from the wires into your hand. The plug must therefore be made of material that does not allow electricity to flow. Compare the properties of the materials listed in the chart. Draw a conclusion about which materials would

be good for making plugs. _____

_____

2. Explain why you chose those materials. _____

_____

_____

_____

3. List two materials that would be good to use for wires to carry electricity in a

circuit and explain why. _____

_____

Harcourt

What Is Electric Energy?

Lesson Concept

Electric energy is the movement of electrons between areas that have opposite charges. When objects with opposite charges are close enough together or when the charges are very large, electrons move between the objects. Electric current moves through an electric circuit. When electric current flows through a conductor, it produces a magnetic field, turning the conductor into an electromagnet.

Vocabulary

electric charge (C70)	**electric force** (C71)	**electric current** (C71)
conductor (C72)	**electric circuit** (C73)	**insulator** (C73)
resistor (C73)	**electromagnet** (C74)	

Match the term in the left column with its description in the right column.

_____ **1.** positive charge

_____ **2.** static electricity

_____ **3.** series circuit

_____ **4.** proton

_____ **5.** electric energy

_____ **6.** electric current

_____ **7.** conductor

_____ **8.** generator

_____ **9.** electron

_____ **10.** resistor

_____ **11.** electric force

_____ **12.** negative charge

A the energy produced by the movement of electrons

B an atomic particle with a negative charge

C the charge an object has when it has gained electrons

D the charge an object has when it has lost electrons

E the attraction or repulsion that unlike or like charges have

F the potential electric energy of a charged object

G an atomic particle with a positive charge

H the flow of electrons

I a circuit with only one path for the electrons

J a material that carries electrons easily

K a source of electrons

L a material that resists electric current

Harcourt

Name _____

Date _____

The Path of Reflected Light

Materials

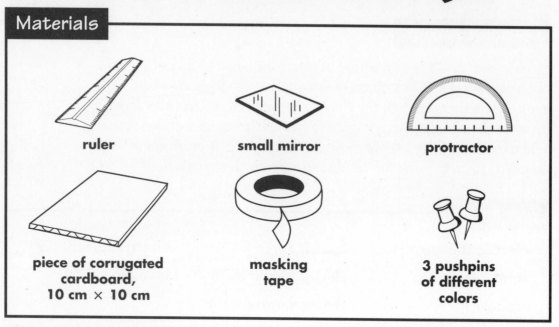

ruler

small mirror

protractor

piece of corrugated
cardboard,
10 cm × 10 cm

masking
tape

3 pushpins
of different
colors

Activity Procedure

1. Lay the cardboard flat. Use the tape to attach the mirror vertically to one end of the cardboard. Push two of the pins into the cardboard, about 5 cm from the mirror.

2. Position yourself at eye level with the mirror. Align yourself so that your view of one pin lines up with the reflection of the other pin. Push a third pin into the cardboard at the edge of the mirror, right in front of where you see the reflection of the second pin. The first pin, the third pin, and the reflection of the second pin should appear to be in a straight line.

3. Draw lines on the cardboard to connect the three pins. These lines show how the reflected light from the first pin traveled to your eye.

4. Using the protractor, **measure** the angle between each line and the edge of the mirror. You will probably have to trace the edge of the mirror and then move it out of your way to make this measurement. **Record** your results.

5. Now remove the original pins and place two of them 10 cm from the mirror. Repeat Steps 2–4 with this new arrangement of pins. **Measure** the angles of the new lines, and **record** your results.

Harcourt

Name _____

 **Investigate Log**

6 Now draw diagrams to **communicate** the results of the two experiments. Each diagram should show the locations of the pins and the mirror and the path of the reflected light.

Draw Conclusions

1. Compare the two angles you **measured** in each experiment.

_____

_____

2. The angle at which light strikes a mirror is the *angle of incidence*. The angle at which it reflects from the mirror is the *angle of reflection*. **Draw a conclusion** about the angle of incidence and the angle of reflection from a flat surface.

_____

_____

_____

3. Scientists at Work When scientists **observe** a pattern that seems to always be true, it helps them **predict** what will happen in the future. Predict what the angles of incidence and reflection would be if the pins were 20 cm from the

mirror. _____

_____

Investigate Further Hypothesize, or develop a testable question, about how light would be reflected from a mirror that was not flat. Then **plan and conduct a simple investigation** to test your hypothesis or answer your question.

_____

_____

_____

_____

Harcourt

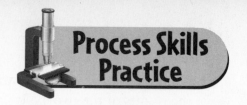

Predict

When you predict, you anticipate outcomes of future events, basing
your ideas on your prior experience, observations, or knowledge.

Think About Predicting

Louise was given a toy guitar for her birthday. She noticed that plucking on the
thicker strings made a sound lower in pitch than the sound made by plucking on
the thinner strings. She also noticed that if she tightened a string, the sound it
produced would become higher in pitch. She also noticed that all the strings on
her mother's guitar produced sounds lower in pitch than the strings on her toy
guitar. She observed that all the strings on her mother's guitar were longer than
the strings on her toy guitar.

   Louise inferred from her observations that the thinner, the shorter, or the
tighter the string, the higher the pitch of its sound. She thought she could use this
inference to predict the sounds that other stringed instruments would make.

1. What is Louise trying to predict? _____

_____

2. What information does she have that will help her predict? _____

_____

3. A cello is a stringed instrument that looks like a very large violin. What could
   Louise predict about the sounds that a cello might make? Explain.

   _____

   _____

4. Louise knew that a piano is a stringed instrument. What could she predict
   about the strings that would be hammered when she played the keys that

   produce low-pitched sounds? _____

   _____

5. If you used Louise's observations, what could you predict about the sounds
   different-sized drums might make? Explain your answer by using Louise's

   inference. _____

   _____

   _____

Use with page C77.

Concept Review

What Are Light and Sound Energy?

Lesson Concept

Light energy is electromagnetic energy that travels through space and through certain materials. When light waves strike an obstacle, they are absorbed, reflected, or refracted. Lenses are curved pieces of transparent matter that refract light rays. Sound energy is vibrations that travel through matter. Solids and liquids conduct sound better than gases.

Vocabulary

reflection (C78)	**refraction** (C78)	**lens** (C79)
pitch (C81)	**volume** (C81)	

Choose the answer that best completes each statement.

1. A ____ lens is thicker in the middle than at the edges.

  A concave   **B** convex   **C** reflection

2. The bending of light rays is called ____.

  A reflection   **B** absorption   **C** refraction

3. When light rays bounce off an object, the bouncing is called ____.

  A absorption   **B** refraction   **C** reflection

4. The colors of light that objects ____ are the colors we see.

  A absorb   **B** reflect   **C** refract

5. Sound waves have two parts, compression and ____.

  A rarefaction   **B** refraction   **C** reflection

6. Light energy moves as waves called ____.

  A magnetic waves   **B** vibrating waves   **C** electromagnetic waves

7. The ____, the colored part of the eye, narrows and widens to control the amount of light entering the eye.

  A pupil   **B** iris   **C** cornea

Harcourt

Heat Flow

Materials

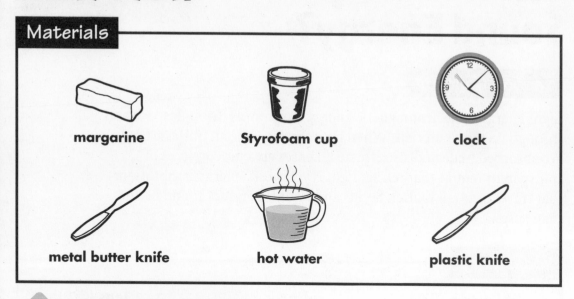

margarine

Styrofoam cup

clock

metal butter knife

hot water

plastic knife

 CAUTION

Activity Procedure

1 Place a dab of cold margarine near the middle of the metal knife. Place another dab of margarine the same size near the tip of the knife's blade.

2 **CAUTION** **Be careful when pouring the hot water.** Half-fill the cup with hot water. Put the metal knife's handle into the water. The dabs of margarine should be above the level of the water.

3 **Predict** which dab of margarine will melt first—the one near the middle of the knife or the one near the end of the knife.

4 **Observe** the metal knife for ten minutes and **record** your observations.

5 Repeat Steps 1–4 using the plastic knife.

6 **Experiment** to find out which material transfers heat faster—metal or plastic. Be sure to **identify and control variables** that might affect the results.

Harcourt

Name _____

Draw Conclusions

1. **Draw conclusions** about how heat moves through the metal knife.

   _____

   _____

   _____

2. **Draw conclusions** about which material transfers heat faster.

   _____

   _____

3. **Scientists at Work** Scientists must **identify and control variables** in an experiment to see how changing one variable affects the results. What variables did you control in your experiment? What variable did you test?

   What was the dependent variable? _____

   _____

   _____

   _____

   _____

   Investigate Further Experiment to find out which knife cools faster. Decide what equipment you will need. _____

   _____

   _____

   _____

Harcourt

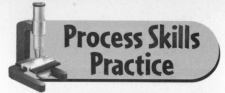

Process Skills Practice

Identify and Control Variables

When you identify and control variables that affect the outcome of an experiment, you state which factors could affect the outcome of the experiment and you make sure that only one of those factors, or variables, is changed in any given test.

Think About Identifying and Controlling Variables

Suppose you are an architect trying to design an energy-efficient house. You want to know which wall and ceiling insulating materials work best so the house can be cooled and heated as inexpensively as possible. You also want lots of windows in the house so you can take advantage of natural light during the day. Windows, however, are where a house loses most of its warmed or cooled interior air. So you want windows that are good insulators but still allow light to pass through freely. You have a choice of three wall and ceiling insulating materials, and you have a choice of two window materials. You decide to build several small buildings the size and shape of doghouses for your test.

1. What are you testing? _____

_____

2. What are some variables in your tests? _____

_____

_____

_____

_____

_____

_____

3. Which of the variables will you control? _____

_____

_____

4. Will using doghouse-sized models give you accurate results? Explain.

_____

_____

_____

_____

Harcourt

Name _____

Date _____

Concept Review

What Are Thermal and Chemical Energy?

Lesson Concept

Thermal energy is the kinetic energy of molecules. The average kinetic energy of the molecules in an object is the object's temperature. Heat is the transfer of thermal energy from one object to another. Conduction is the direct transfer of heat between objects that touch. Convection is the transfer of heat through currents in a gas or a liquid. Radiation is the transfer of energy by electromagnetic waves. When atoms join to form molecules, thermal energy can be stored as chemical energy. Chemical energy can be released as kinetic energy.

Vocabulary

temperature (C86)   **heat** (C86)   **conduction** (C87)

convection (C87)   **radiation** (C87)

Fill in each blank with a vocabulary term. You may use each term more than once.

1. When you add _____ to an object, you increase the kinetic energy of the object's molecules, increasing its _____.

2. If you leave a metal stirring spoon in a pot of soup while the soup is heating, the spoon will quickly get hot because of _____.

3. When you sit near a campfire, the heat of the fire is transferred to you mostly by _____.

4. If your house is heated by a furnace that blows hot air into the rooms, you are depending on the process of _____ to stay warm.

5. A lizard sometimes stretches out on a rock to warm itself. The rock is warm because the sun has transferred thermal energy to it by _____.
The rock then transfers thermal energy to the lizard by _____.
The rock also transfers thermal energy to air above it through a process called
_____.

Harcourt

Use with page C89.

Workbook   WB171

Recognize Vocabulary

Write the letter of the definition in the right column next to the
term that it matches in the left column.

_____ 1. conductor

_____ 2. temperature

_____ 3. electric circuit

_____ 4. lens

_____ 5. electric current

_____ 6. convection

_____ 7. potential energy

_____ 8. heat

_____ 9. insulator

_____ 10. electric charge

_____ 11. pitch

_____ 12. electromagnet

_____ 13. refraction

_____ 14. energy

_____ 15. electric force

_____ 16. radiation

_____ 17. conduction

_____ 18. resistor

_____ 19. volume

_____ 20. reflection

_____ 21. kinetic energy

A a magnet formed by the flow of electric current

B energy of motion

C a material that doesn't carry electrons

D what an object gets when it gains or
loses electrons

E the loudness of a sound

F the average kinetic energy of all the molecules
in an object

G the transfer of thermal energy by
electromagnetic waves

H energy an object has because of its condition

I a quality determined by the speed of
vibration of sound waves

J a material that conducts electrons easily

K light that bounces off an object

L the attraction or repulsion between objects
with a positive or negative charge

M the direct transfer of thermal energy between
objects that touch

N the bending of light rays

O the ability to cause changes in matter

P the flow of electrons

Q the transfer of thermal energy from one
substance to another

R a piece of clear material that bends light rays
passing through it

S the transfer of thermal energy through
currents in a liquid or a gas

T a material that resists the flow of electrons

U any path along which electrons can flow

Harcourt

Use with pages C62–C89.

Chapter 1 • Graphic Organizer for Chapter Concepts

Renewable and Nonrenewable Resources

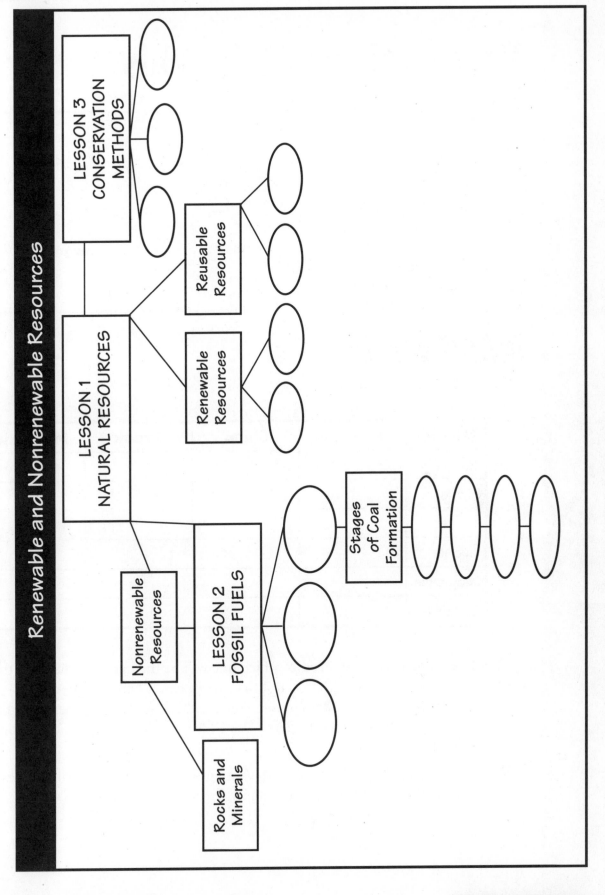

Name _____

Date _____

Investigate Log

Properties of Minerals

Materials

6 mineral samples
(talc, pyrite, quartz, fluorite,
magnetite, graphite)

tile

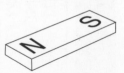

magnet

Activity Procedure

1 Use the following chart.

Mineral	Hardness	Shine	Streak	Magnetic
talc				
pyrite				
quartz				
fluorite				
magnetite				
graphite				

2 **Observe** each mineral. **Predict** which one will be the hardest. Then rub the minerals against each other to test their hardness. A harder mineral will scratch a softer one. Under *Hardness* on the chart, write a number from 1 to 6 for the hardness of each mineral. Use 1 for the softest mineral. Use 6 for the hardest mineral.

3 **Observe** each mineral, and decide whether or not it is shiny. Write *yes* next to the name of the mineral if it is shiny. Write *no* if it is not.

Harcourt

Name _____

④ Now **predict** the color of the streak
each mineral will make. A streak is the colored line a mineral makes when it
is rubbed on a tile. Then rub each mineral on the tile. If the mineral makes a
streak, write the color of the streak next to the mineral's name. Write *none* if
the mineral does not make a streak.

⑤ Finally, **predict** which minerals will be attracted to a magnet. Test each
mineral with a magnet. Write *yes* next to the names of minerals that stick
to the magnet. Write *no* next to the names of those that do not.

Draw Conclusions

1. Which mineral is the softest? **Compare** your test results with your predictions.

_____

_____

_____

2. Which minerals make streaks? **Compare** your test results with your color

predictions. _____

_____

_____

3. Which minerals are magnetic? **Compare** your test results with your

predictions. _____

_____

4. **Scientists at Work** Scientists often **predict** what might happen. How did
careful observations of the mineral samples help you make better predictions

about their properties? _____

_____

_____

Investigate Further Use the data you recorded on each mineral's properties to

infer its uses. _____

_____

_____

_____

Harcourt

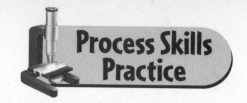

Predict

One way to check your understanding of something is to predict an outcome, and then see how closely your prediction matches the actual outcome. The first step is to interpret the data you have collected.

Think About Predicting

In 1955 each farm worker in the United States produced enough food to feed 20 people. By 1960 farming methods had improved, and one worker could supply 25 people. In 1965 that number became 40 people. In 1970 it was 45 people. In 1975 it increased to 60 people. In 1980 one farm worker could supply 75 people. Graph this data in the grid to the right to show how production increased with time. Then use the graph to help you predict.

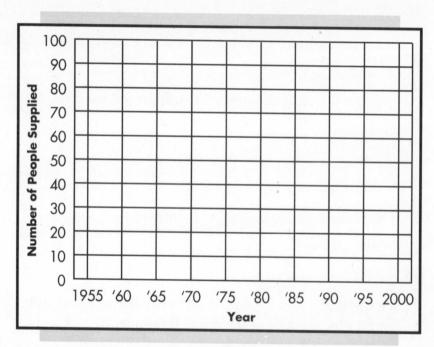

1. How many people do you think were supplied by one farm worker in 1990?

   _____

   _____

2. Will a graph like this help you predict far into the future? Why or why not?

   _____

   _____

   _____

Harcourt

Name _____

Date _____

What Are Natural Resources?

Lesson Concept

Natural resources are useful materials that people take from Earth.
Some resources are renewable or reusable. Others are nonrenewable.
Once nonrenewable resources are used, they cannot be replaced.

Vocabulary

natural resource (E6)   **nonrenewable resource** (E6)

renewable resource (E8)   **reusable resource** (E8)

Next to each resource listed below, write whether the resource is
renewable, reusable, or nonrenewable. Explain your answer.

Resource	Type and Explanation
1. water	_____
2. oil	_____
3. wood	_____
4. soil	_____
5. gasoline	_____

Harcourt

Use with page E9.

What Kinds of Rocks Store Petroleum?

Materials

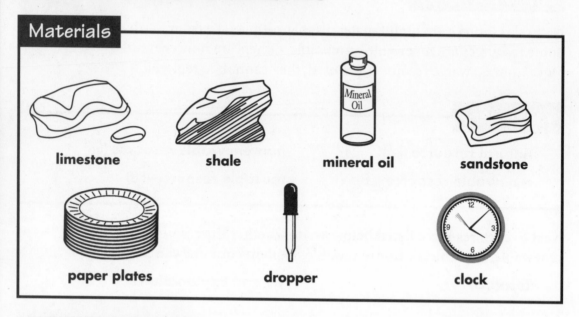

limestone   shale   mineral oil   sandstone

paper plates   dropper   clock

Activity Procedure

1. Place the rock samples on separate paper plates. **Observe** each rock. **Predict** which will be the best storage rock.

2. Fill the dropper with mineral oil. Put 5 drops of oil on the limestone sample.

3. **Observe** and **record** the time it takes for the 5 drops of oil to soak into the limestone.

4. Continue adding oil, counting the drops, until the limestone will hold no more oil. **Record** the number of drops it takes.

5. Repeat Steps 2–4 with the other rock samples.

Harcourt

Draw Conclusions

1. Which rock soaked up the oil the fastest? What was the time?

_____

_____

2. Which rock soaked up the most oil? What was the number of drops?

_____

_____

3. Which rock is the best storage rock? Explain how you came to this conclusion. What other information do you need to support this conclusion?

_____

_____

_____

4. Scientists at Work Scientists often **use numbers** to **compare** things. How did you use numbers to compare the oil-storing ability of the rocks?

_____

_____

Investigate Further Develop a testable question about which of the rocks might be a source rock for petroleum. Decide what equipment you would need, and then make quantitative observations about each rock. _____

_____

_____

_____

Harcourt

Name _____

Date _____

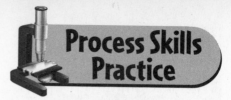

Use Numbers and Compare

Numbers give you a way to estimate things. They allow you to count, order, or compare information.

Think About Using Numbers and Comparing

The table below on the left shows how many quadrillion Btus (a way of measuring energy) were used in 1995 by the countries listed. Find the largest number in the "Btus" column. Put that number at the top of the Btus column in the table on the right. Next to that number, write the name of the country that used that amount of energy. Complete the table, ordering the numbers from largest to smallest.

Country	Btus
Germany	13.71
United Kingdom	9.85
China	35.67
Italy	7.42
Russia	26.75
Canada	11.72
United States	90.94
Japan	21.42
France	9.43
India	10.50

Btus	Country

1. What is the total energy used by the five European countries listed? What is the total energy used by the three Asian countries? How do these figures compare?

   _____

   _____

2. What did you learn from adding and comparing the numbers showing

   European and Asian energy use? _____

   _____

   _____

Harcourt

How Do Fossil Fuels Form?

Lesson Concept

Fossil fuels form over millions of years from the decayed remains of organisms. Coal forms in four stages, first forming peat, then lignite, then bitumen, and finally anthracite.

Vocabulary

peat (E14)   **lignite** (E14)   **bitumen** (E15)

anthracite (E15)   **natural gas** (E13)   **fossil fuels** (E12)

Write the letter of the definition in Column B next to the word or phrase it explains in Column A.

Column A

_____ 70 percent

_____ anthracite

_____ the sun

_____ sedimentary

_____ petroleum

_____ bitumen

_____ swamps

_____ coal

_____ seams

_____ fossil fuels

_____ natural gas

_____ lignite

_____ peat

_____ petrochemicals

Column B

A coal, natural gas, and petroleum

B the most common fossil fuel

C fossil fuel that formed when microorganisms died and fell to the bottoms of ancient seas

D first stage of coal formation

E soft, brown rock that forms as layers of sand and mud cover peat

F mostly methane, usually found with petroleum

G source of the energy in fossil fuels

H third stage of coal formation

I chemicals made from petroleum

J kind of rock in which fossil fuels are usually found

K layers of coal

L fourth stage of coal formation

M places where peat can be found

N amount of carbon in lignite

Harcourt

How People Use Natural Resources

Materials

small bowl of paper clips

3 generation cards
(parents, children, grandchildren)

Activity Procedure

1. Work in a group of three. Place your group's generation cards face down on a table. The bowl of paper clips stands for Earth's supply of a certain resource, such as iron.

2. Each person in the group now takes a generation card. Hold up your card so the other people in your group can see it. The card tells you your generation. It also tells you how many people are in your generation.

3. Each generation will now get paper clips from the bowl. The person from the parents' generation goes first. He or she takes five clips from the bowl for each person in his or her generation.

4. Next, the person from the children's generation takes five clips for each person in his or her generation.

5. Finally, the person from the grandchildren's generation takes five clips for each person in his or her generation.

Harcourt

Name _____

Draw Conclusions

1. Did everyone get the same number of clips? _____

2. Where did a problem occur? _____
_____

3. What could be done to avoid the problem? _____
_____

4. **Scientists at Work** Scientists **hypothesize** what the results of an investigation might be. Hypothesize what will happen if each person from a generation gets only three or four clips, instead of five. _____
_____
_____
_____

Investigate Further With the members of your group, list the products people use that are made from a natural resource, such as a certain metal. Describe several things people could do to make sure that in the future there will be enough of this resource. Then select and use appropriate tools and technology to simulate your plan. _____
_____
_____
_____
_____

Harcourt

Name _____

Date _____

Hypothesize

A hypothesis is an educated "guess" about how one thing will be affected by another thing. A hypothesis is based on observation and prior knowledge. It can be tested in an experiment and changed depending on the result of the experiment.

Think About Hypothesizing

In some places trucks pick up newspapers, glass, cans, and plastics to be recycled. In other places people must take these items to a recycling center. In some states people get money back when they recycle certain types of glass or plastic bottles. Some towns put up billboards reminding people to recycle. What makes people more likely to recycle?

1. Think about the following hypothesis: If you pay people to recycle, then more people will recycle. How could you test this hypothesis?

_____

_____

2. What results would support the hypothesis? _____

_____

_____

_____

3. Some people hypothesize that if you make recycling easier for people, then they will recycle. How can you test this hypothesis? _____

_____

_____

4. Some people hypothesize that if you educate people about the importance of recycling, then they will recycle. How can you test this hypothesis? _____

_____

_____

5. Hypothesize which of the three methods given above would be most effective in getting people to recycle. Support your hypothesis. _____

_____

_____

Harcourt

How Are Natural Resources Conserved?

Lesson Concept

Earth has a limited supply of natural resources, which must be conserved so that they will last as long as possible. One way to conserve resources is to reduce the amounts that are used. Another way is to reuse things. Many things that can't be reused can be recycled.

Vocabulary

recycling (E22)

Think of things you could do to conserve resources by reducing, reusing, or recycling. Next to each resource below, describe what you could do to conserve that resource.

Reduce

1. Gasoline _____

_____

_____

2. Coal (Electricity) _____

_____

_____

_____

Reuse

3. Plastics _____

_____

_____

Recycle

4. Trees (Paper) _____

_____

Use with page E23.

Harcourt

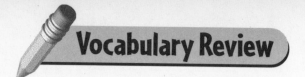
Recognize Vocabulary

Review the vocabulary terms for Chapter 2 by completing this word puzzle.

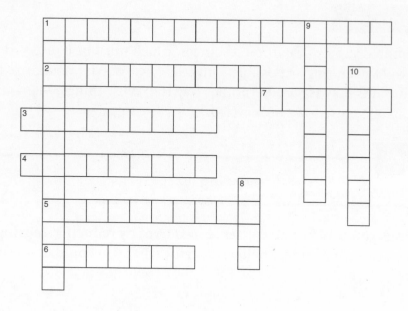

Across

1. Minerals and other useful materials that are taken from Earth (2 words)
2. A fossil fuel consisting mostly of methane (2 words)
3. A resource that's replaced as it is used is called a _____ resource.
4. The process of taking back the resource in a product
5. A very hard, black rock that is the most valuable form of coal
6. This is formed when pressure squeezes moisture out of peat
7. Burned to heat homes and produce electricity, _____ fuels are formed from decayed organisms in Earth.

Down

1. A resource that cannot be replaced is called a _____ resource.
8. A soft, brown material made up of partially decayed plants
9. A resource that can be used more than once is called a _____ resource.
10. The most common type of coal mined and used today

Harcourt

Chapter 2 • Graphic Organizer for Chapter Concepts

How People Use Energy

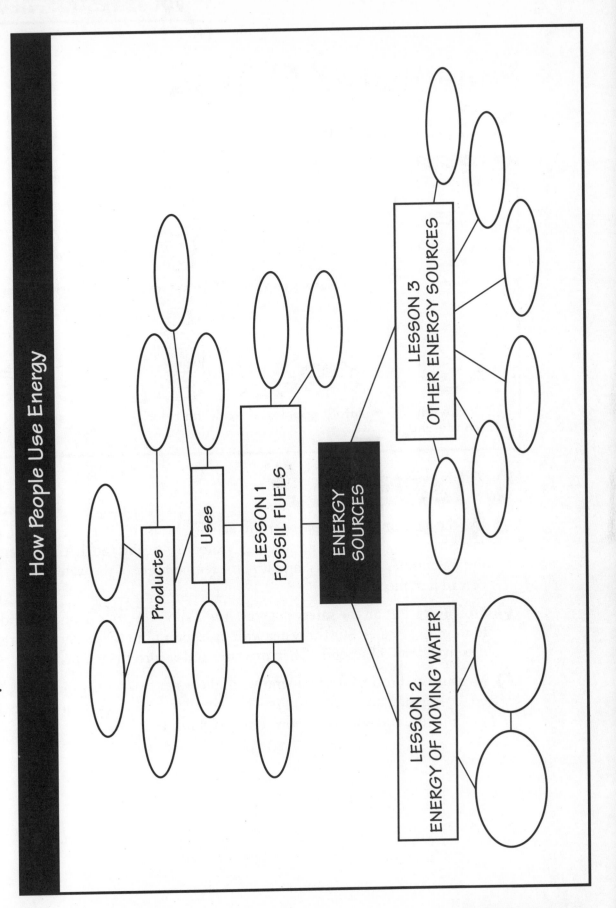

Name _____

Date _____

How Stored Energy Is Released

Materials

water

measuring cup

Styrofoam cup

thermometer

clock with second hand

safety goggles

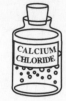
calcium chloride

spoon

 CAUTION

Activity Procedure

1 Use the table on the next page for this activity. Measure 50 mL of water in the measuring cup, and pour it into the Styrofoam cup. Put the thermometer in the water. After 30 seconds, **measure** the temperature of the water and **record** it in the table.

2 **CAUTION** Put on the safety goggles. Add 2 spoonfuls of calcium chloride to the cup of water. Stir the water with the spoon until the calcium chloride dissolves. Wait 30 seconds. Then **measure** and **record** the temperature.

3 **Measure** and **record** the temperature of the water two more times, after 60 seconds and after 120 seconds. Then **compare** the temperature of the water before and after you added calcium chloride.

Harcourt

Substance	Temperature
Water without chemical	
Water with chemical after 30 seconds	
Water with chemical after 60 seconds	
Water with chemical after 120 seconds	

Draw Conclusions

1. How did the temperature of the water change when you added calcium chloride? _____

2. **Infer** whether the calcium chloride gives off heat or absorbs heat as it dissolves in water. _____

3. What do you **infer** might have caused the water temperature to change?

   _____

   _____

4. **Scientists at Work** Scientists **observe** and **measure** to gather as much data as they can from an experiment. What did you learn from this experiment about how the chemical energy in some compounds can be released?

   _____

   _____

Investigate Further Hypothesize what will happen when different chemicals, such as sodium chloride (table salt) or magnesium sulfate (Epsom salts), are placed in water. **Plan and conduct a simple investigation** to test your hypothesis. Be sure to write instructions others can follow to carry out the procedure. Then classify the reactions as *exothermic* (giving off heat), *endothermic* (taking in heat), or *no reaction*. _____

_____

_____

_____

Harcourt

Name _____

Date _____

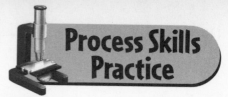

Observe and Measure

When you observe, you use one or more of your senses to perceive properties of objects and events. One type of observing is measuring. When you measure, you are making observations with the aid of instruments, such as stopwatches or thermometers.

Think About Observing and Measuring

Before you can effectively measure anything, you have to know what you will be measuring. Then you choose the appropriate instrument for the type of measuring you will be doing. In the following questions, you will be asked to make those decisions.

1. You are working for a veterinarian. It is your job to feed the dogs. Your instructions are to feed each dog twice a day, one-half cup at each feeding for every 15 pounds that the dog weighs. What observations will you be making,

and what measuring instruments will you be using? _____

_____

_____

2. You are part of a mapping expedition that is going into unexplored territory. The expedition plans to take a boat up the river until it reaches the river's source. Your job is to map the course of the river for later expeditions. What observations will you make? What instruments and what units of measure will

you use? _____

_____

_____

_____

3. A local television station has asked you to be part of a weather watch. They expect you to call the station every day at 4:00 P.M. and tell them the temperature, sky conditions, the wind speed, and any other observation you think might be important. What will you be observing and what instruments will you use?

_____

_____

_____

_____

Harcourt

How Do People Use Fossil Fuels?

Lesson Concept

Coal, natural gas, and petroleum are fossil fuels formed from once-living matter that has been buried for millions of years. Fossil fuels are used to heat homes, move cars, and generate electricity. Because fossil fuels take millions of years to form, they are nonrenewable.

Vocabulary

chemical bonds (E34)

Answer each question with one or more complete sentences.

1. How did energy from sunlight become stored in fossil fuels?

_____

_____

2. How does burning fuel of any kind turn solar energy into thermal energy?

_____

_____

_____

3. Why are fossil fuels the main source of energy for so many people?

_____

4. Where is most of the chemical energy in living organisms stored?

_____

_____

5. What type of fossil fuel is the main source of energy for transportation?

_____

6. Give at least two reasons other sources of energy besides fossil fuels should be used. _____

_____

_____

Harcourt

Water Power

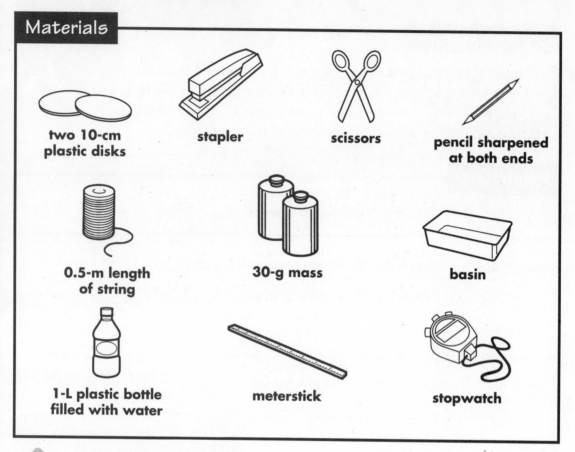

two 10-cm plastic disks

stapler

scissors

pencil sharpened at both ends

0.5-m length of string

30-g mass

basin

1-L plastic bottle filled with water

meterstick

stopwatch

CAUTION Activity Procedure

1 **CAUTION** **Be careful when using the scissors.** Staple the plastic disks together near their centers. Using the scissors, cut four 3-cm slits into the disks as shown on page E39. At each slit, fold the disks in opposite directions to form a vane.

2 Again using the scissors, punch a 0.5-cm hole at the center of the disks. Insert the pencil. It will serve as the axle on which the water wheel rotates.

3 Use the scissors to make a smaller hole next to the pencil hole. Insert one end of the string into the hole, and tie a knot in the string to keep it in place. Tie the mass to the other end of the string.

4 Place the basin near the edge of the desk. Hold your water wheel over the basin. Your fingertips should hold the pencil points so the pencil can turn. The mass on the string should hang over the edge of the desk.

Harcourt

Name _____

 **Investigate Log**

5 Have a partner slowly pour water over the wheel from a height of about 10 cm. Using the stopwatch, **measure** and **record** the time it takes for the mass to reach the level of the desk. Repeat this step several times.

6 Now repeat Steps 4 and 5, but have your partner pour the water from a height of about 20 cm. Again, **measure** and **record** the time it takes for the mass to reach the level of the desk.

Draw Conclusions

1. What **variables** did you **control** in your investigation? _____

_____

What variable did you change? _____

_____

2. Recall that the greater the power, the more quickly work is done. Which of your trials produced more power? Why? _____

_____

3. **Scientists at Work** Scientists often look beyond the results of an investigation. For example, how does the height from which the water is poured affect the speed at which the water wheel turns? **Plan and conduct a simple investigation** to find out. Be sure to **identify and control variables** so that you have only a single, independent variable to test. _____

_____

_____

_____

_____

Investigate Further Hypothesize about the rate of flow and the speed at which the water wheel turns. Then **plan and conduct a simple investigation** to test your hypothesis. Be sure to **identify and control variables**. Write instructions others can follow to carry out the procedure. _____

_____

_____

_____

Harcourt

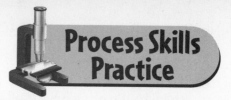

Identify and Control Variables

Identifying and controlling variables involves stating or controlling factors that affect the outcome of an experiment. It is important that only one variable be altered in any given test.

Think About Identifying and Controlling Variables

Read the descriptions of experiments below. Then identify the variable that is altered in each experiment, and explain what scientists could learn by controlling variables in the experiment.

1. People noticed that the number of a certain type of fish that live in a river seemed to have decreased since a dam was built on the river. Scientists who were concerned about the situation captured some of the fish and put them in giant tanks to study them. Both tanks were filled with river water. Plants, rocks, and insects from the river were also introduced into each tank. In one tank the water was 8 meters deep, the average depth of the undammed river. The water in the other tank was 30 meters deep, the depth of the river behind the dam.

_____

_____

2. Many fish died in both tanks in the investigation in Question 1. Trying to determine the cause of the fish deaths, the scientists set up two tanks, each with 8 meters of water in it. New fish were introduced, along with stones, insects, and plants from the river. One tank was lit by light that simulated sunshine.

The other was kept dark. _____

_____

_____

3. Patricia built two water wheels by placing a dozen plastic slats between two plastic coffee-can lids. On one water wheel, she placed the slats so they pointed straight to the center from the edge of the lids. On the other wheel, she placed the slats so they were tilted at a sharp angle from the edge of the coffee-can lids. Using a pencil as the axle, she suspended each wheel over a basin and asked an assistant to pour water over them at a steady rate from 10 centimeters above the wheel. _____

_____

_____

Harcourt

How Can Moving Water Generate Electricity?

Lesson Concept

An electric generator changes mechanical energy to electric energy. One source of this mechanical energy is moving water. Hydroelectric energy stations use the energy of falling water to spin turbines that generate electricity. The mechanical energy present in ocean tides can also generate electric energy.

Vocabulary

hydroelectric energy (E40)   **tidal energy** (E42)

Write a phrase from the chart to complete each sentence .

hydroelectric energy can be traced back to the sun
the potential energy of water under pressure
by holding back water at high tide and letting it fall through turbines at low tide
of falling water to spin turbines that generate electricity
to electric energy
the turbine spins the shaft of an electric generator
can also generate electric energy

1. An electric generator changes mechanical energy _____ .

2. The energy that spins a hydroelectric turbine comes from _____

_____ .

3. Hydroelectric energy stations use the energy _____

_____ .

4. The mechanical energy present in ocean tides _____

_____

Harcourt

Name _____

Date _____

A Steam-Powered Turbine

Materials

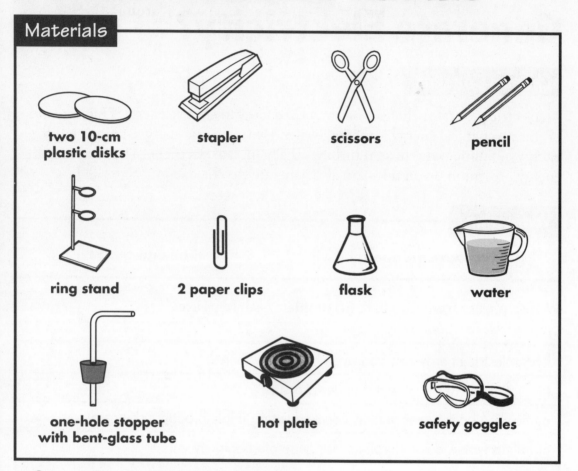

two 10-cm plastic disks

stapler

scissors

pencil

ring stand

2 paper clips

flask

water

one-hole stopper with bent-glass tube

hot plate

safety goggles

Activity Procedure

1 You can modify the water wheel you made in the last investigation by adding 12 more vanes to the wheel and enlarging the hole. Or you can follow Steps 2 and 3 to make your turbine.

2 **CAUTION** **Be careful when using the scissors.** Staple the plastic disks together near their centers. Using the scissors, cut sixteen 3-cm slits into the disks as shown on page E45. At each slit, fold the disks in opposite directions to form a vane.

3 Again using the scissors, cut a 0.5-cm round hole in the center of the disks. Make the hole as round as possible. Insert the pencil. It will serve as the axle on which the turbine rotates. The turbine should spin freely on its axle. Now suspend the axle and turbine from the ring stand arm with two bent paper clips.

Harcourt

Name _____

 Investigate Log

4 Fill the flask with water. Put the stopper with the bent glass tube in the flask. Set the flask on the hot plate. Point the open end of the glass tube toward the vanes on the bottom of the turbine.

5 **CAUTION** **Put on the safety goggles, and use caution around the steam.** Turn on the hot plate. **Observe** and **record** your observations of the turbine as the water begins to boil. Draw a diagram of your turbine to **communicate** your results. Be sure to include labels and arrows to show what happens.

Draw Conclusions

1. **Infer** the source of energy for turning the turbine. _____

_____

2. **Communicate** in several paragraphs how the energy from the source was changed to turn the turbine. Include tests you conducted, data you collected, and your conclusions. _____

_____

_____

_____

3. **Scientists at Work** When scientists **communicate**, they try to show clearly or describe what is happening. In what two ways did you communicate the results of this investigation? Which way was clearer? _____

_____

_____

Investigate Further Plan and conduct a simple investigation to determine how much work your turbine can do. Decide what questions you will need to answer and what equipment you will need to use. Write instructions others can follow to carry out the procedure. _____

_____

_____

_____

Harcourt

Name _____

Date _____

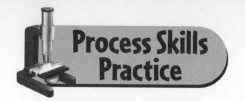

Communicate

Communicating involves the passing on of data. This may be done through spoken or written words, graphs, drawings, diagrams, maps, and charts. Communicating in science means showing the results of an activity in an organized fashion so the results can later be interpreted or the activity can be repeated.

Think About Communicating

In the questions below, you will find four types of information that a scientist might want to communicate. In the space provided, describe what you think would be the best way to communicate the information.

1. A laboratory was studying the nutritional requirements of a new breed of mouse they had developed for cancer research. They discovered that the healthiest mice were those fed a diet consisting of 15 percent protein, 75 percent carbohydrates, and 10 percent fats. What sort of graph, drawing, or

   chart would best communicate these results? _____

   _____

2. A group of scientists was surveying a large open area for the placement of windmills. They wanted to be sure each windmill would receive the greatest amount of wind possible, so they placed wind vanes in the area and kept track of the wind speed and direction over a period of six months. Then they took the average for each position. What would be the best way for them to

   communicate their results? _____

   _____

3. A fisher was keeping track of the height of the tides in a certain area as part of a study being done at a local university. He drove a long measuring stick into the ground at the water's edge at low tide. Then, every hour, he checked the water's depth on the measuring stick. What kind of graphic would best

   communicate what he discovered? _____

   _____

4. Scientists were studying the relative top running speeds of animals in East Africa. They clocked a cheetah at 100 kilometers per hour (km/hr), a gazelle at 72 km/hr, a wildebeest at 36 km/hr, a leopard at 65 km/hr, and a jackal at 40 km/hr. What would be the best way to communicate this information?

   _____

Harcourt

Name _____

Date _____

Concept Review

What Other Sources of Energy Do People Use?

Lesson Concept

In addition to fossil fuels and hydroelectric energy, the United States uses small amounts of energy from other sources. These sources include biomass, nuclear energy, wind, geothermal energy, and solar energy. Researchers continue to work on new sources of energy, such as fusion.

Vocabulary

nuclear energy (E46)   **biomass** (E46)   **solar energy** (E47)

fusion energy (E48)   **geothermal energy** (E47)

List the advantages and disadvantages of each type of energy.

Type of Energy	Advantages	Disadvantages
Biomass		
Nuclear		
Solar		
Wind		
Geothermal		
Ocean Thermal		
Hydrogen		

Harcourt

Use with page E49.

Recognize Vocabulary

Choose one of the words from the box to answer each riddle.

biomass	nuclear energy
hydroelectric energy	solar energy
geothermal energy	chemical bonds
fusion energy	tidal energy

1. I'm alive now, or I was fairly recently. Burning me doesn't release a lot of energy, but I'm free or very inexpensive, so a lot of people use me. What am I?

   _____

2. I'm not a wallet, and I'm not a purse or a backpack. I'm not a bank account, but I'm the thing that all living things keep their "saved-up" energy in. What am I?

   _____

3. Look for me at Niagara Falls or Glen Canyon Dam! I'm on the Missouri River and the Tennessee River, too. What am I? _____

4. Atoms are very tiny, but if you split them apart, you'll get me, the most powerful source of thermal energy on Earth. What am I? _____

5. If you want to get your energy directly from the source, you'll come to me. Too many cloudy days, however, could make it hard for you to get enough of me. What am I? _____

6. Dig deep to find me, preferably near a volcano or an earthquake zone. What am I? _____

7. I result from something that happens twice a day. See you at the beach! What am I? _____

8. I'm in the experimental stages. Scientists know how I work, but the heat needed to get me started is so high that it burns all known materials. What am I?

   _____

Harcourt